Nanostructure
and
Nanomaterials

Nanostructure and Nanomaterials

Editor

B.K. Parthasarathy

ISHA BOOKS
Delhi-110009

Nanostructure and Nanomaterials

© B.K. Parthasarathy

ISBN: 81-8205-428-1

Published in 2007 in India by
ISHA Books
B-63, 1st Floor, New Gupta Colony,
Near DDA Market,
Delhi-110009
Phone: 9212142040
ishabooks@hotmail.com

Laser Type Setting by: Rudra Computer Graphics, Delhi
Printed at: Salasar Imaging System, Delhi

Preface

One often hears of nanotechnology being heralded as one of the most fascinating and promising fields of science to emerge in the last century. Indeed, with its potential to miniaturise the world we live in through the control of matter in the range of 1-100 nanometres, it is no surprise that nanotechnology holds the potential to completely revolutionise the way we live. It has already made great inroads in the fields of biotechnology, life sciences, medicines, pharmaceuticals, agriculture, engineering, etc. and promises to do more.

This book has been written so that it serves as a valuable guide into the world of nanostructures and nanomaterials, which form the premise on which the rest of nanomarvels rest. Nanotechnology can be thought of as extensions of traditional disciplines towards the explicit consideration of these properties. Additionally, traditional disciplines can be re-interpreted as specific applications of nanotechnology. This dynamic reciprocation of ideas and concepts contributes to the modern understanding of the field. Broadly speaking, nanotechnology is the synthesis and application of ideas from science and engineering towards the understanding and production of novel materials and devices. These products generally make copious use of physical properties associated with small scales. Materials reduced to the nanoscale can suddenly show very different properties compared to what they exhibit on a macroscale, enabling unique applications. For instance, opaque substances become transparent (copper); inert materials become catalysts (platinum); stable materials turn combustible (aluminum); solids turn into liquids at room temperature (gold); insulators become conductors (silicon). All these concepts and principles contribute vastly to our understanding of how nanostructures function the way they do, and how they how they are further manipulated into and manifested as nanomaterials like fullerenes and nanocrystals.

The book serves the function of aiding an insightful and thorough discussion of what entails the numerous aspects of nanostructures, the bottom-down and top-down approaches to constructing them, the techniques, practices and the sciences involved in this regard, and how they eventually culminate in nanomaterials. Emphasis has also been placed upon the what various manifestations of nanomaterials into nanoproducts, and what they project for the future. The various issues relating to it, which include the social and biological implications of nanotechnology, have also ben detailed. In addition, the book brings under cover the ethical, legal and scientific ramifications of nanostructures and nanomaterials. Compendious and exhaustive, it is hoped that the book serves well for nano-enthusiasts.

Editor

Contents

Contents

1

Strategies of Nanomaterials

Strategies of nanoparticles and nanomaterials accommodate precursors from liquid, solid, or gas phase. They employ both chemical and physical deposition approaches; and similarly rely on either chemical reactivity or physical compaction to integrate nanostructure building blocks within the final material structure. The "bottom-up" approach of nanomaterials synthesis first forms the nanostructured building blocks (nanoparticles) and then assembles them into the final material.

An ample of this approach is the formation of powder components through aerosol techniques and then the compaction of the components into the final material. These techniques have been used extensively in the formation of structural composite nanomaterials. One "top-down" approach begins with a suitable starting material and then "sculpts" the functionality from the material. This technique is similar to the approach used by the semiconductor industry in forming devices out of an electronic substrate (silicon), utilising pattern formation (such as electron beam lithography) and pattern transfer processes (such as reactive ion etching) that have the requisite spatial resolution to achieve creation of structures at the nanoscale. This particular area of nanostructure formation has tremendous scope and is a driving issue for the electronics industry.

Another top-down approach is "ball-milling," the formation of nanostructure building blocks through controlled, mechanical attrition of the bulk starting material. Those nano building blocks are then subsequently assembled into a new bulk material. In fact, many current strategies for material synthesis integrate both synthesis and assembly into a single process, such as characterises chemical synthesis of nanostructured materials.

The degree of control required over the sizes of the nanostructure components, and the nature of their distribution and bonding within the fully formed material varies greatly, depending on the ultimate materials application. Achieving selective optical absorption in a material may allow a wide range of sizes of the component nanostructure building blocks, while quantum dot lasers or single electron transistors require a far tighter distribution of size of the nanostructure components. Compaction methods may provide excellent adhesion for nanocomposite materials of improved structural performance (e.g., ductility), but such interfaces may be unsatisfactory for electronic materials.

Methods for the synthesis of nanoparticles can be divided into three main groups.

1.   Synthesis of semiconductor nanoparticles in solutions of the corresponding salts by controlled addition of anions (or cations) or by hydrolysis.
2.   Preparation of nanoparticles as a result of phase transformations.
3.   The synthesis of nanoparticles in aerosol.

The radiation-chemical method for the synthesis of nanoparticles is also known. Methods for the synthesis of complex multicomponent nanoparticles have been developed. Most of the semiconductor colloidal systems studied to date have been obtained by synthesising the semiconductor nanoparticles in homogeneous solution.

Commercial colloidal solutions containing the SnO_2 nanoparticles (with an average diameter of 3 nm) are available from Johnson Matthey (USA). Another commercially available nanoparticle is Degussa P25 TiO_2 powder containing 80% of anatase and 20% of rutile.

Semiconductor Nanoparticles

The semiconductor nanoparticles could be prepared by chemical synthesis in homogeneous solutions, in different surfactant assemblies like micelles, vesicles, and Langmuir-Blodgett films, in polymers, glasses, zeolites, and β-cyclodextrin. The easiest and most common method for the preparation of semiconductor nanoparticles is the synthesis from the starting reagents in solution by arresting the reaction at a definite moment of time. This is the so-called method of arrested precipitation. Nanoparticles of metal sulphides are usually synthesised by a reaction of a watersoluble metal salt and H_2S (or Na_2S in the presence of an appropriate stabiliser such as sodium metaphosphate. For example, the CdS nanoparticles can be synthesised by mixing $Cd(ClO_4)_2$ and Na_2S solutions:

$$Cd(ClO_4)_2 + Na_2S = CdS\downarrow + 2NaClO_4 \qquad (1)$$

The growth of the CdS nanoparticles in the course of reaction is arrested by an abrupt increase in pH of the solution. Colloidal particles of metal oxides can be obtained by hydrolysis of the corresponding salts. For example, the TiO_2 nanoparticles are readily formed in the hydrolysis of titanium tetrachloride

$$TiCl_4 + 2H_2O = TiO_2\downarrow + 4HCl \qquad (2)$$

Formation of TiO_2 nanoparticles via reaction (2) is shown schematically in Figure 2. Unfortunately, most of the colloidal solutions of nanoparticles; have low stability towards coagulation and possess a large size dispersion. Coagulation can be prevented by passivation of the surface of nanoparticles by hydroxyl ions, amines, or ammonia. Yet another procedure for the stabilisation of colloidal solutions of nanoparticles is the coating of their surfaces with polyphosphates or thiols.

As a result, one can obtain a stable colloidal solution of nanoparticles, isolate the nanoparticles as a powder, and then prepare a colloidal solution again by dispersing the powder in a solvent. Usually, the method of arrested precipitation results in a nonuniform size distribution of nanoparticles. It is possible to decrease the width of this distribution by monitoring the synthetic procedures and using high-pressure liquid chromatography and capillary electrophoresis. In the latter case, the separation of nanoparticles is achieved due to the different charge/size ratios for nanoparticles of different sizes. Small monodisperse semiconductor clusters (like e.g. Cd_4S_4) can be obtained by performing the synthesis inside zeolite cages. Larger semiconductor nanoparticles of fixed size could be synthesised by introducing additional molecules to a small initial cluster stabilised by organic ligands in a colloidal solution. For instance, it was found that the size of CdS clusters coated with thiophenolate ions can be increased if a metal sulphide is added to the solution.

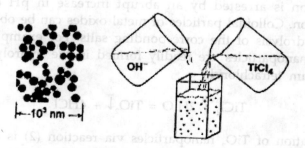

Figure 1. Scheme of TiO$_2$ nanoparticles formation by the method of arrested precipitation.

Such a polymerisation of inorganic compounds appeared to be applicable to the synthesis of large semiconductor clusters of strictly fixed size from small particles like $[Cd_{20}S_{13}(SC_6H_5)_{22}]^{8-}$ clusters containing 55 cadmium and sulphur atoms from the pyramidal $[Cd_{10}S_4(SC_6H_5)_{16}]^{4-}$ clusters containing 30 cadmium and sulphur atoms. The introduction of additional five sulphide ions leads to the fusion of two small clusters into one larger cluster. The process of the formation of a large cluster from two small ones can be illustrated by the following scheme:

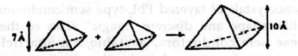

The pyramidal structure of the $[Cd_{20}S_{13}(SC_6H_5)_{22}]^{8-}$ clusters was confirmed by X-ray analysis. Further addition of sulphide ions made it possible to obtain the $Cd_{32}S_{14}(SC_6H_5)_{36}$ tetrahedral clusters containing 82 cadmium and sulphur atoms. Usually, it is assumed that the nanoparticles containing several hundreds of atoms have a spherical or ellipsoidal shape. However, recent investigations have shown that the nanoparticles often have clearly defined facets and their shape is analogous to that of macroscopic crystals. The shape and size of nanoparticles is determined by electron microscopy. For a rough estimation of the size of nanoparticles, it is also possible to use the optical spectra of colloidal solutions. These estimates are based on the dependence of the position of the excitonic band of nanoparticles on their size.

Macroscopic Particles

It is possible to obtain semiconductor nanoparticles by sonication of colloidal solutions of large particles. Nanoparticles of layered semiconductors are also formed upon mere dissolution of large particles in an appropriate solvent, which was observed for MoS_2 and WS_2. Layered MoS_2-type semiconductors are characterised by a weak van der Waals interaction between separate S - Mo - S layers. In the course of dissolution, the solvent molecules penetrate between the layers of the semiconductor and destroy large particles. In the case of MoS_2, the process of destruction can proceed until the formation of a two-layer particle. No further splitting of the semiconductor crystal occurs, since the formation of single-layer particles is accompanied by a considerable increase in the free energy of the system.

Nanocrystals of layered PbI_2-type semiconductors have a disk-like shape and discrete "magic" sizes of the disks. For these semiconductors, a stable nanoparticle of a minimum size is assumed to be the smallest crystallite conserving the hexagonal symmetry of the macroscopic crystal. Such a crystallite is composed of two seven-atom iodine layers and two lead layers. Large stable nanoparticles are obtained from this 'seed' by the layer-bylayer addition of extra iodide 'caps' symmetrically around the perimeter. An analogous structure is also assumed for MoS_2 nano particles.

The gas-phase synthesis could also be used to get nanoparticles. Thus the Si nanoparticles are formed in 67% yield in the combustion of SiH_4 under oxygen-deficient conditions as a result of thermolysis of SiH_4. Another method for the gas-phase synthesis of nanoparticles of various materials is based on the pulsed laser vaporisation of metals in a chamber filled with a known amount of a reagent gas followed by controlled condensation of nanoparticles onto the support. A schematic view of the installation for the synthesis of nanoparticles is given in Figure 2.

As the metal atoms diffuse from the target to the support, they interact with the gas to form the desired compound (for instance, oxide in the case of oxygen, nitride for nitrogen or ammonia, carbide for methane, etc.). The pulsed laser vaporisation of metals in the chamber makes possible to prepare nanoparticles of mixed molecular composition, such as mixed oxides/nitrides and carbides/nitrides or mixtures of oxides of different metals. Along with the reagent gas, the chamber contains an inert gas, such as He or Ar, at a pressure of 10-21 Torr, which favours the establishment of steady convection between the heated bottom plate and cooled top plate. In an experiment with a single pulse of a Nd:YAG laser (532 nm, 15-30mJ/pulse, 10^{-9} s pulse duration), over 10^{14} metal atoms are vaporised.

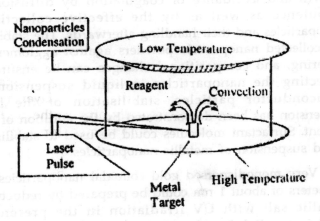

Figure 2. Schematic view of the installation for the synthesis of nanoparticles

A new compound is formed due to the reaction between the 'hot' metal atoms and the gas molecules, which is accompanied by the energy loss of the molecules formed by collisions with the inert gas atoms. The metal atoms that did not enter into reaction and the molecules of the new compound are carried by convection to the nucleation zone on the cooled top plate. By changing the composition of the inert gas and the reagent gas in the chamber and varying the temperature gradient and laser pulse power, it is possible to control the elemental composition and size of nanoparticles that are obtained. One of the most challenging problems in synthesis is the controlled generation of monodispersed nanoparticles with size variance so small that size selection by centrifugal precipitation or mobility classification is not necessary.

Among all the synthesis techniques discussed above, gas-phase synthesis is one of the best techniques with respect to size monodispersity. In this method, monodispersity is typically achieved by using a combination of rigorous control of nucleation/condensation growth and avoidance of coagulation by diffusion and turbulence as well as by the effective collection of nanoparticles and their handling afterwards. The stability of the collected nanoparticle powders against agglomeration, sintering, and compositional changes can be ensured by collecting the nanoparticles in liquid suspension. For semiconductor particles, stabilisation of the liquid suspension has been demonstrated by the addition of polar solvent. Surfactant molecules could be used to stabilise the liquid suspension of metallic nanoparticles.

Very monodispersed gold colloidal nanoparticies with diameters of about 1 nm could be prepared by reduction of metallic salt with UV irradiation in the presence of dendrimers. Poly(amidoamine) dendrimers with surface amino groups of higher generations have spherical 3-D structures, which may have an effective protective action for the formation of gold nanoparticles. Although the specific role of dendrimers for the formation of monodispersed nanoparticles has yet to be defined, good monodispersity is thought to come from the complex reaction accompanying the decomposition of dendrimers, which eventually leads to the conversion of solution ions to gold nanoparticles.

The high efficiency of recombination of the light-generated electrons and holes presents obstacles to the practical application of the semiconductor nanoparticles in photocatalysis. In this connection, the semiconductor nanocrystal hetero-structures composed of semiconductors with different structures of the electronic levels are of considerable interest. With these structures, it is possible to attain high quantum yields of charge separation.

The nanoparticles schematically shown in Figure 4 belong to this class of hetero-structures. The structures analogous to that shown in Figure 4A are known for CdS/TiO_2, CdS/ZnO, CdS/AgI, CdS/HgS, Cd_3P_2/TiO_2, Cd_3P_2/ZnO, and AgI/Ag_2S. For CdS/TiO_2, photoexcitation into the absorption band of US results in the electron transfer from CdS to TiO_2, while the hole remains in CdS. These structures are also of interest as nanoscale rectifier units for molecular electronics. The formation of hetero-structures of the 'core-shell' type has been demonstrated using the $CdSe/ZnS$ and $ZnS/CdSe$ nanoparticles as an example. These nanoparticles are obtained by controlled precipitation of semiconductor molecules of one type ('shell') on the pre-synthesised nanoparticles of another type ('core'). The synthesis of the shell is carried out in colloidal solution by methods analogous to those for the synthesis of one-component nanoparticles, considered above. The crystalline shells grow on the nanocrystal core despite the fact that the lattice constants in CdSe and in ZnS differ by 13%.

Nanostructured Semiconductor Films

Thin films of semiconductor nanoparticles are of considerable practical interest. Synthesis of these films is carried out by precipitation of pre-formed nanoparticles from colloidal solutions onto the supports, by direct precipitation of semiconductor molecules onto the support, and by oxidative hydrolysis of the corresponding metal salts at the anode. Usually, the films are 0.1 -1 μm thick. The following films of semiconductor nanoparticles are known: SnO_2, ZnO, TiO_2, WO_3, and Fe_2O_3. The SnO_2, ZnO,

TiO_2, and WO_3 films were obtained by precipitation of nanoparticles.

Direct precipitation of semiconductor molecules onto the support is used to prepare films of nanoparticles of semiconductors on the basis of Group II-VI elements. Oxidative hydrolysis of $TiCl_3$ at pH 2.3 and a platinum anode potential of 0 V vs. saturated calomel electrode results in the formation of nanoparticles with an average diameter of 1-2 nm on the anode surface. Nanostructured films containing nanoparticles of different semiconductors can be prepared by co-precipitation. A schematic view of such a film supported by the optically transparent electrode is given in Figure 3.

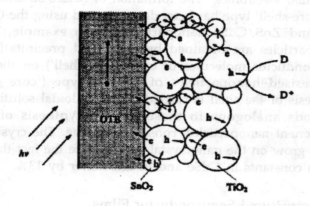

Figure 3. Schematic view of the process of photostimulated charge separation in the nanostructured Film composed of TiO_2 and SnO_2 nanoparticies adsorbed on an optically transparent electrode (OTE).

Yet another method for the preparation of such films consists in wetting of a plate coated with a film of a certain type of nanoparticles with a solution containing metal ions followed by wetting of the plate with a solution containing sulphide ions. This procedure was used for the synthesis of films containing ZnO and CdS nanoparticies.

Recent paradigm shift envisioned for optoelectronics and computational devices involves the assembly of molecular or quantum wires. Chain aggregates of nanoparticles can be considered as polymer-like units with their primary particles composed of a few hundred to a few thousand molecules.

Depending on the particle size and its compositional material, the bonding force responsible for holding the aggregates together varies from weak van der Waals force for micrometer particles to strong chemical bonds for nanometer particles. The mechanical, optical, and electronic transport properties of these wires can be varied by controlling the diameter and the monodispersity of the primary particles, the crystalline structure, aggregate length, interfacial properties, and material purity.

Membranes, with nanochannels generated by fission-fragment tracks or by electrochemical etching of aluminum metal, are used as templates for either chemical or electrochemical deposition of conductive polymers, metals, and semiconductors for the generation of nanofibers or tubes. Since the nanochannels on membranes are very uniform in size, the diameter and the aspect ratio of the nanofibers (or tubes) synthesised by the membrane template technique can be precisely controlled.

Singlecrystal semiconductor nanofibers can also be grown catalytically by metalorganic vapour phase epitaxy and laser ablation vapour-liquid-solid techniques. These methods allow to synthesise one dimensional structures with diameters in the range of 3 to 15 nm. The advent of carbon-based nanotubes has created yet another way to fabricate nanometer fibers and tubes. These nanotubes have been used as templates for the fabrication of carbide and oxide nanotubes.

The carbon nanotubes can now be catalytically produced in large quantities and have been used for reinforcement of nanostructural composite materials and concrete.

Carbon Nanotubes

Carbon nanotubes are unique nanostructures with remarkable electronic and mechanical properties. Interest from the research community first focused on their exotic electronic properties, since nanotubes can be considered as prototypes for a onedimensional quantum wire. As other useful properties have been discovered, particularly strength, interest has grown in potential applications.

Carbon nanotubes could be used, for example, in nanometer-sized electronics or to strengthen polymer materials. An ideal nanotube can be thought of as a hexagonal network of carbon atoms that has been rolled up to make a seamless cylinder. Just a nanometer across, the cylinder can be tens of microns long, and each end is "capped" with half of a fullerene molecule. Single-wall nanotubes can be thought of as the fundamental cylindrical structure, and these form the building blocks of both multi-wall nanotubes and the ordered arrays of single-wall nanotubes called ropes. Figure 4 shows an image of a fragment of a one-wall carbon nanotube. The nanotubes could be prepared by the laser vaporisation of a carbon target in a furnace at 1200 °C.

A cobalt-nickel catalyst helps the growth of the nanotubes, presumably because it prevents the ends from being "capped" during synthesis, and about 70-90% of the carbon target can be converted to single-wall nanotubes. By using two laser pulses 50 ns apart, growth conditions can be maintained over a larger volume and for a longer time. This scheme provides more uniform vaporisation and better control of the growth conditions. Flowing argon gas sweeps the nanotubes from the furnace to a water-cooled copper collector just outside of the furnace.

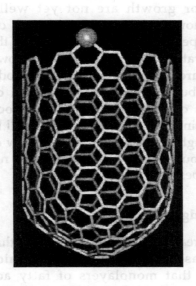

Figure 4. A fragment of a one-wall carbon nanotube.

A carbon-arc method has been developed to grow similar arrays of single-wall nanotubes. In this case, ordered nanotubes were also produced from an ionised carbon plasma, and joule heating from the discharge generated the plasma. In a scanning electron microscope, the nanotube material produced by either of these methods looks like a mat of carbon ropes. The ropes are between 10 and 20 nm across and up to 100 μm long. When examined in a transmission electron microscope, each rope is found to consist of a bundle of single-wall carbon nanotubes aligned along a single direction. X-ray diffraction, which views many ropes at once, also shows that the diameters of the single-wall nanotubes have a narrow distribution with a strong peak.

While multi-wall carbon nanotubes do not need a catalyst for growth, single-wall nanotubes can only be grown with a catalyst. However, the detailed mechanisms responsible for growth are not yet well understood. Experiments show that the width and peak of the diameter distribution depends on the composition of the catalyst, the growth temperature and various other growth conditions. Great efforts are now being made to produce narrower diameter distributions with different mean diameters, and to gain better control of the growth process. From an applications point of view, the emphasis will be on methods that produce high yields of nanotubes at low cost, and some sort of continuous process will probably be needed to grow carbon nanotubes on a commercial scale.

Langmuir-Blodgett Films

Following the realisation of Lord Rayleigh that a film of oil on water was just one molecule thick Langmuir demonstrated that monolayers of fatty acids could be ordered on the surface of water by application of pressure undergoing phase changes from a gaseous state of non-interacting molecules to a "solid" state where the molecules interacted in a rigid film.

Langmuir and Blodgett realised the transfer of such monolayers from the water surface to a solid substrate by slowly passing an appropriately treated substrate through the air/water interface. Figure 7 schematically shows the deposition of Langmuir-Blodgett film from a floating Langmuir monolayer. In practice films are spread on an ultra clean water sub phase in a teflon trough in a clean room (class 100).

The trough has a moveable teflon barrier straddling the air water interface and this is controlled mechanically to compress the film under servocontrol. As the surface area of the film is thus reduced the surface pressure of the film increases. The pressure-area isotherm is monitored continuously and at some area/molecule the pressure will begin a rapid increase as the solid phase is reached while the area per molecule remains approximately constant.

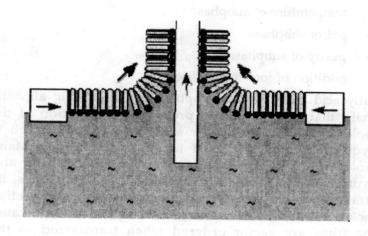

Figure 5. Deposition of Langmuir-Blodgett film from a floating Langmuir monolayer

If the pressure increases much further the film will be liable to collapse. At some predetermined pressure in the solid phase the film pressure is held steady. A substrate may now be passed through the air/water interface and as monolayers are picked up the film area will reduce. The pressure is held constant by feedback from a pressure monitor and the reduction of area is monitored to find a transfer ratio, (area of slide covered)/(loss of area from film on trough). Ideally this should be 100% but it may be greater (if for example the molecules are slowly dissolving into the sub phase) or less if incomplete coverage of the slide is achieved.

If the first is occurring this should be noticed by monitoring the area of the film for some time before attempting to transfer a monolayer. If the area is gradually reducing this would suggest that the molecules are either dissolving into the sub phase or leaking under the barrier. Many factors may influence film-forming characteristics some of which are:

— temperature of subphase
— pH of subphase
— purity of subphase
— addition of ions to stabilise films.

Fatty acid molecules are amphiphilic with a long aliphatic chain that is hydrophobic preventing dissolution of the molecule and a carboxylic acid head group, which is hydrophilic attaching itself to the water surface. Many molecules with this arrangement of hydrophilic and hydrophobic moieties will for Langmuir Blodgett films. By attaching such parts to an electro or optically active molecule a functionalised molecule may be made. Because the films are vector ordered when transferred to the substrate multilayers with desired electro/optical properties may be assembled.

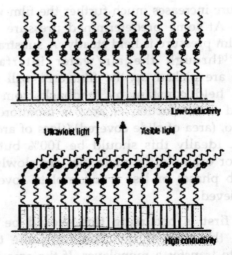

Figure 6. The conductivity of LB film can be switched by the irradiation of light.

Langmuir-Blodgett (LB) films, constructed by transferring monolayers floating on water surface to a solid substrate, are expected to be widely applied to molecular electronic and bioelectronic devices because of characteristics such as the thickness and molecular arrangement being controllable at the molecular level. As an example, Figure 8 shows Langmuir-Blodgett film that has different conductivity upon illuminating by the light. Illumination of the fatty acid molecules presented in this figure changes the molecular conformation from cis to trans (visible light) or from trans to cis (UV light) thus changing the electrical conductivity of the molecule.

Biogenic Strategies

The ability of amphiphilic molecules to self organise in aqueous solutions could be used to produce nanomaterials in which self-assembled organic materials are used as templates or scaffolding for inorganic components. As one example of such selfassembled or self-organised materials, McGehee et al. have mixed silica precursors with surfactants that have self-ordered to form various surfactantwater liquid crystals.

A range of various structures built from walls of amorphous silica was observed. These structures are organised about a repetitive arrangement of pores up to a hundred angstroms in diameter. This example shows that the addition of organic molecules can strongly influence the resulting structure of inorganic components. Such strategies have been adopted in synthetic formation of nanostructures, such as in the formation of networks of gold clusters. The methodology of self-assembly has even been extended to physical vapour deposition processes where it would seem more difficult to control the nucleation and growth of three-dimensional nanostructures. Utilising the strain inherent in the epitaxial growth of lattice-mismatched materials, and the expected strain-induced transition from two-dimensional (layered) to three-dimensional (islanded) growth, researchers have been able to form arrays of semiconductor quantum dots (~20-30 nm in diameter, ~10^{11} cm^{-2} in density, a size variation of about ±7%). The achievement of arrays of several billions of quantum dots of these dimensions with such a size variation is beyond the capability of standard high resolution lithographic and pattern transfer processes.

Moreover, the controlled formation of critical surfaces and interfaces without the intercession of ion-assisted processing that can introduce potential defects into the materials has produced a rich source of optically and electronically efficient quantum structures. Such self-assembled dots have already incorporated into laser structures. Chemical specificity may provide the most robust means of ensuring control of size and placement of nanostructured building blocks. Recent work in the synthesis of compound semiconductor quantum dots from chemical precursors have provided even tighter distributions of size variation (±5 %) than those shown in the strain-induced selfassembled dots.

2
Synthesis of Nanomaterials

Over the past twenty years, developments in instrumentation such as the Atomic Force Microscope (AFM), Scanning Tunneling Microscope (STM), and High Resolution Transmission Electron Microscope (HRTEM) have allowed scientists to observe and manipulate nanostructures. Diatoms comprise a large group of photosynthetic eukaryotic microorganisms characterised by the presence of a unique siliceous frustule, or wall, composed of opaline silica, in essence, a biologically produced glass (silicate, SiO_2).

The diatom frustule is typically composed of two relatively large pieces, the valves, joined together by several linking elements, and the girdle. Valves and, in many cases, girdle elements are perforated by a variety of openings and passageways that permit the exchange of material between the living components of the cell and the external environment. In the simplest case, the openings take the form of pores or tubes through the solid matrix of the valve or girdle element.

Among the more complex structures are loculate chambers, which are large openings in the valve matrix partially, occluded by a thickening of the wall on one side and by a siliceous velum on the other? Vela come in many forms, including perforated plates (cribra), suspended solid discs (rotae), and flap-like outgrowths of the valve wall (volae). The openings range in size from a few nanometers in diameter for simple pores and individual pores in a cribral plate to several micrometers in diameter for the loculate chambers of larger diatoms. The symmetry and diversity of diatom frustules have attracted the attention of biologists since the earliest days of microscopy.

Currently, over 10,000 species have been described, with the true diversity estimated to be much greater, possibly as many as 100,000 or even 1,000,000 species. Species are recognised primarily on the basis of shape and arrangement of the valves and the valvar perforations. These can be arranged into three large taxonomic groupings. Centric taxa are characterised by a more or less radially symmetric valve shape and arrangement of valvar openings. The symmetry derives from the presence of a ring or annulus, which forms the basis of the primary wall. In araphid pennate diatoms, the annulus is replaced by a longitudinal sternum.

The primary wall then grows outward from the sternum, imparting a bilateral symmetry to the valve. In raphid pennate diatoms, the longitudinal sternum is replaced by a more complex structure containing one or two slits or raphes. The basic structure is, again, bilateral. More complex shapes and morphologies can usually be traced back to one of these three-growth forms. The siliceous elements of the diatom wall are formed in special subcellular structures called silica deposition vesicles (SDV). The process seems to involve the precipitation of silicic acid into spherical particles 35 to 50 nanometers in diameter.

The particles join together to form the structure of the valve, beginning with either a ring or a longitudinal rib (the annulus and sternum mentioned previously). Deposition proceeds from the initial structure in an array of growing, branching ribs. In diatoms with complex valve structures, additional siliceous layers may form and attach to the primary layer. While the sequence of events is fairly well understood, the mechanisms that give rise to the complex symmetries and arrangements of pores is not. Suggested mechanisms include the presence of a structure external to the SDV that helps to shape and mold the SDV itself and the presence of organic templates or chemical gradients within the SDV that direct the deposition of the colloidal particles of silica. Both living diatoms and their siliceous remains are important in commercial settings.

Living diatoms are used as feedstock in aquaculture and as indicators of environmental conditions. Their remains, in the form of diatomite and diatomaceous earth, have a number of properties that make them particularly suitable for a number of commercial applications: low density, high porosity, low thermal conductivity, high melting point, and chemical inertness. Over 300 commercial applications for diatomite and diatomaceous earth have been documented. The fine pores in the frustules make them especially useful in filtration and about 73% of diatomite is used for this purpose.

Other applications include insulation, fine abrasion, pesticide, and inert filler. More recently, applications of diatoms in nanotechnology have been suggested. One approach is to use the mechanisms underlying cell wall deposition to direct the formation of novel siliceous component. A second approach, used here, is to use the symmetrical fine structure of the valve as a mold or template for the construction of microscopic components of more complex machinery.

For many applications in nanotechnology, from electronics to fibers, carbon nanotubes have become the standard starting point. While they have some known advantages for specific applications, they also have a number of disadvantages that will limit their use in the bulk production of many chemicals or crystals. Carbon nanotubes will also react and breakdown in the presence of oxidising agents such as ozone and hydrogen peroxide.

They are relatively expensive ($500 U.S. dollars per gram) and have limited geometric possibilities (i.e. tube structures 1.4 to 2 nm diameter).

Diatoms offer a number of potential advantages as templates for nanostructures. With a large number of species and subsequently geometries and pore sizes naturally occurring, specific geometries can be obtained. Diatoms can be harvested or grown in bulk so processes that may require large amounts of the material are feasible. Their silicate-based shell is unreactive in the presence of strong acids or oxidising agents. Mn_{12}, a molecular magnet, is a manganese-based cluster that is synthesised in an aqueous environment and incorporate oxide and acetate anions in its inner and outer spheres.

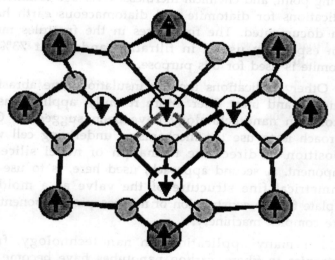

Figure 1. The $Mn(IV)_4Mn(III)_8O_{12}$ core of Mn_{12} has four Mn atoms with a spin down and eight Mn atoms with a spin up. The twelve unlabeled atoms are oxygen.

The well-known molecular systems that are characterised as nanomagnets are Mn_{12} and Fe_8, each with Spin (S) = 10. Mn_{12} was the first proven example but recent, lesser known examples include Mn_4, Fe_8, V_4, Fe_4, Fe_{10}, Mn_{10} and Fe_{19} cages. All of these single molecule magnets (SMMs) retain their spin orientation in the absence of a magnetic field and have been dubbed nanoscale magnetic memory devices.

Molecular magnets exhibit no exchange couplings between individual clusters. Leuenberger and Lossargue that the potential for SMMs is enormous. For example, SSMs can store magnetic information in 10-20 metal centres rather than in a metal particle representing a 10^5 decrease in size. They also suggest SMMs can be used in quantum computing because SMMs also exhibit quantum tunneling, a physical phenomenon in which the duality of nanoparticles as a particle and as a wave can be clearly observed. In Mn_{12} there are eight Mn^{+3} ions ($3d^4$, $S = 2$) that give an $S = 16$, and there are four Mn^{+4} ($3d^3$, $S=3/2$) cations that give an $S=6$. The sum of these twelve Mn cations yield a total spin (S) = $8(2) - 4(3/2) = 10$, indicating four inner ions ($S=3/2$) with their spins pointing in one direction and eight outer ion spins pointing in the opposite direction ($S=2$) (Figure 1).

All Mn_{12} molecules in the sample have the same total spin, have different properties in different directions (anisotropic), the same controlled geometric orientation, and present a well-defined mesoscopic magnet which, on a macroscopic scale, produce the quantum properties of a single molecule. Mn_{12} has provided the first experimental evidence of macroscopic quantum tunneling. Its magnetisation relaxes between two sublevels which are separated by an energy barrier. At high temperatures, reversals of the magnetic moment occur. At an intermediate temperature there is enough thermal energy for the magnetisation direction of particles to start reversing which results in the material being composed of approximately equal amounts of magnetically split and unsplit components. This temperature is called the blocking temperature (T_B).

T_B's are obtained by analysing the zero field cooled (ZFC) and field cooled (FC) susceptibility versus temperature curve.

$$\tau^{-1} = f_o \, exp \, (-E_a/k_B T) \tag{1}$$

where τ is the relaxation time, T is temperature in Kelvin, E_a is the anisotropy barrier, k_B is Boltzmann's constant, and f_0 is a frequency factor. E_a can be determined by $E_a = KV$ in which K is the anisotropy energy density constant, and V is the volume of particle. The dc magnetisation reflects the blocking in the difference between the zero-field-cooled magnetisation (where the sample is cooled in zero field below the blocking temperature, and then a field is applied and the magnetisation is measured as a function of increasing temperature) and the field-cooled magnetisation (where the magnetisation is measured upon cooling in a field). The T_B of a superparamagnetic particle system is estimated from

$$T_B = E_a/k_B \, \ln(t \, f_o) \tag{2}$$

Where t is the experimental measuring time. Typically, k_B $\ln(t \, f_o)$ can be considered constant over a given set of experiments. T_B is measured by determining the peak position of ZFC susceptibility versus temperature. Often, the interactions between magnetic particles are ignored and the susceptibility data are analysed without considering the interparticle distance or the density of particles. In reality these parameters can influence the interparticle magnetic interaction in the nanoparticle systems.

Dai and coworkers studied how applied pressure and sample density affect the magnetic properties of an iron oxide nanoparticle system, specifically how the T_B of γ-Fe_2O_3 is changed by compression. They demonstrated that if the interaction between individual particles is included, the energy barrier and the blocking temperature will change to:

$$T_B = (E_a + E_{int})/k_B \ln(tf_o) \tag{3}$$

where E_{int} is an interaction energy, and will be a key parameter in explaining the T_B data for Mn_{12} synthesised in various mediums. Murata and coworkersmeasured the impact of pressure on Quantum Tunneling of Magnetisation (QTM) of Mn_{12}. They demonstrated QTM is quenched as pressure is exerted on the crystal.

As interactions between clusters increase, the blocking temperature will increase, and if the clusters are pulled slightly apart, a decrease in the T_B would be expected. In comparing the different media for Mn_{12} growth, we must consider that if the cluster is adsorbed or nucleates onto the surface of a graphitic structure (NTs, EG) or a silica structure (diatoms, silica) and subsequently becomes compressed (shorten Mn-O bond) or slightly distorted (lengthen Mn-O bond), this would account for shifts in T_B. Hysteresis loops involve measuring magnetisation verses field for powders or crystals. Ferromagnets will stay magnetised after being subjected to an external magnetic field.

The ability to remember its magnetic history is called hysteresis. When a ferromagnetic material is magnetised in one direction, it will not relax back to zero magnetisation when the imposed magnetising field is removed. It must be forced back by a field in the opposite direction. If an alternating magnetic field is applied to the material, its magnetisation will trace out a loop called a hysteresis loop. Mn_{12} is somewhat unusual because it has a stepped magnetisation curve in which discrete movements of electrons within the energy barriers can be observe.

Exfoliated Graphite and Carbon Nanotubes

Carbon nanotubes and fullerenes can be synthesised by several methods including carbon arc, carbon vapour, and laser abalation. Carbon nanotubes, 2-4 nanometer in diameter, can have metallic or semiconducting characteristics as well as an extremely high tensile strength.

Ozone (O_3) is a strong oxidising agent (E_o = 2.07 V) that attacks and breaks carbon-carbon double bonds and leaves behind carboxylates, carbonyls and may result in CO or CO_2 gas. In their work the researchers open the SWNT with ozone so a pore exists for the solution containing Mn_{12} to enter the carbon based capillary tube. SWNTs typically have length/diameter ratios greater than 1000 making them ideal nano-capillary tubes.

Their experiments were based on trying to grow silver particles in a diatom matrix. They wanted to use a spontaneous oxidation-reduction reaction (eq.6) involving zinc metal and silver cation dissolved in an acidic solution to see what geometry of Ag(s) would be produced.

$$Zn(s) + 2Ag^+(aq) \Rightarrow Zn^{+2}(aq) + 2Ag(s)$$

$$E^o_{cell} = +1.56 \text{ V} \tag{4}$$

Typically silver will form a solid without any defined shape when precipitated from an aqueous phase reaction. In a diatom matrix (pH = 2.0), the reaction formed small hairs or rods of silver on the order of 1-2 um in width. Optical microscopy allowed absolute identification of these structures due to their dramatic silver colour and electron microscopy allowed us to closely investigated and record the rod like structures. This result is encouraging since the normal aggregation process produces a range of shapes and sizes.

A series of experiments were centered on trying to understand the growth mechanism of the Mn_{12} crystal. Specifically, we wanted to combine the substrate (diatoms, EG, etc.) with Mn_{12} entrap or catch the Mn_{12} crystals in the early stages of nucleation. If the substrate is added too early, the Mn_{12} crystals might adsorb on the surface of the diatom or graphic material and the desired crystal size would not be achieved. If the substrate is added too late, the Mn_{12} crystals will grow to the micrometer or millimeter size range.

This data led us to believe the synthesis takes place in three basic steps: oxidation and reduction to form the Mn^{+3} and Mn^{+4} ions in solution (eq. 5a), the formation of individual Mn_{12}-Ac clusters (eq. 5b), and the growth and formation of Mn_{12} crystals (eq. 5c)

$$KMnO_4(s) + Mn(Ac)_2*4H_2O(s) \Leftrightarrow Mn^{+3}(aq) + Mn^{+4}(aq)$$

$$Mn^{+3}(aq) + Mn^{+4}(aq) \Leftrightarrow Mn_{12} \text{ Clusters}$$

$$Mn_{12} \text{ Clusters} \Leftrightarrow Mn_{12} \text{ crystals}$$

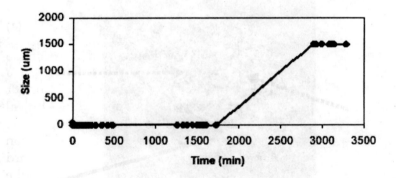

Figure 2. The size of Mn_{12} crystals monitored by laser diffraction.

They used SEM and HRTEM to measure the Mn_{12} crystals size on various substrates. Mn_{12} crystals grown in the diatom matrix were typically in the one to ten micron range and, and 20-1000 times smaller than the crystals observed in pure Mn_{12} (Fig. 3).

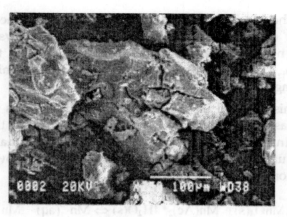

Figure 3. A SEM image (250 X magnification) of pure Mn_{12} crystals.

While this average size reduction was encouraging, the goal was for the Mn_{12} clusters absorb into the diatom pores and form particles a few nanometers in size.

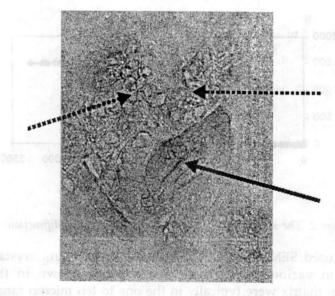

Figure 4. HRTEM image shows one of the EG packets (solid arrow) that has opened and expelled Mn_{12} crystals (dotted arrows).

HRTEM images showed a number of EG packets in which the graphitic sheets encapsulated the Mn based compounds (figure 4). EG, when immersed in the acetic acid solution used to synthesise the Mn_{12}, become individual sheets and adsorb Mn_{12} clusters. As the solution dries, the EG sheets entrap the Mn_{12} clusters.

Synthesis of Polymer Nanocomposites

Polymer nanocomposites are materials in which nanoscopic inorganic particles. Systems in which the inorganic particles are the individual layers of a lamellar compound—most typically a smectite clay or nanocomposites of a polymer (such as nylon) embedded among layers of silicates—exhibit dramatically altered physical properties relative to the pristine polymer. For instance, the layer orientation, polymer-silicate nanocomposites exhibit stiffness, strength and dimensional stability in two dimensions (rather than one). Due to nanometer length scale which minimises scattering of light, nanocomposites are usually transparent.

Polymer nanocomposites represent a new alternative to conventionally filled polymers. Because of their nanometer sizes, filler dispersion nanocomposites exhibit markedly improved properties when compared to the pure polymers or their traditional composites. These include increased modulus and strength, outstanding barrier properties, improved solvent and heat resistance and decreased flammability. Polymers that contain transition metal complexes either attached to or directly in a π-conjugated backbone are an exciting and a promising class of modern materials. These macromolecules are hybrid of π-conjugated organic and transition metalcontaining polymers. π-conjugated organic polymers, such as polyacetylene, polythiophene, and polypyrrole, as well as oligomers and derivatives of these materials have been extensively explored. These materials are endowed with many important properties such as nonlinear optical properties, electronic conductivity and luminescence, and have been proposed for their use in various applications including chemical sensors, electroluminescent devices, electrocatalysis, batteries, smart windows and memory devices. Layered silicate/polymer nanocomposites exhibit superior mechanical characteristics (e.g. 40% increase of room temperature tensile strength), heat resistance (e.g. 100% increase in the heat distortion temperature) and chemical resistance (e.g. ~10 fold decrease in O_2 and H_2O permeability) compared to the neat or traditionally filled resins.

These property improvements result from only a 0.1-10 vol.% addition of the dispersed nanophase. Polyimide-clay hybrids represent another example of polymer nanocomposites. These nanocomposites have been prepared by intercalation of the organoclay with a polyamic acid. The claypolyimide hybrid composite films exhibit greatly improved CO_2 barrier properties at low clay content; less than 8.0 vol. % clay results in almost a ten-fold decrease in permeability.

Adding nanoscale ceramic powders to commercial products can produce another class of polymer nanocomposites. The addition of reinforcing agents is widely used in the production of commodities (packaging films and tyres). It is expected that the reduction of the added particle size down to nanometric scale could enhance the performance of these materials, even though not to the extent as layer addition. These new materials are aimed at being a substitute for more expensive technical parts (gear systems in wood drilling machines, wear resistance materials) and in the production of barrier plastic film for food industry. Besides structural applications, polymer nanoparticle compounds have very interesting functional applications. For instance, γ-Fe_2O_3/ polymer nanocomposites are used as advanced toner materials for high quality colour copiers and printers and as contrast agents in NMR analysis, memory devices. The key to forming such novel materials is understanding and manipulating the guest-host chemistry occurring between the polymer and the layered compounds or the nanoparticles, in order to obtain a homogenous dispersion and a good contact between polymer and added particle surfaces.

There have been major advances in solid state and materials chemistry in the last two decades and the subject is growing rapidly. The coatings of magnetic particles are of special interest because of their important applications viz. technological energy transformation, magnetic recording, magnetic fluids and magnetic refrigeration system. Polymer materials have been filled with several inorganic compounds in order to increase properties like heat resistance, mechanical strength and impact resistance and to decrease other properties like electrical conductivity, dielectric constant thereby increasing the permeability for gases like oxygen and water vapour.

In recent years considerable efforts have been devoted to the development of methods for the preparation of composite particles consisting of polymer cores covered with shells of different chemical composition. In several of these powders, particles covered with magnetic materials have been used as beads for gas separation, or as pigments, catalysts, coatings, flocculents, toners, raw materials recovery, drug delivery and anticorrosion protection. Polymer composites containing ferrites are increasingly replacing conventional ceramic magnetic materials because of their mouldability and reduction in cost. They are also potential materials for microwave absorbers, sensors and other aerospace applications.

These flexible magnets or rubber ferrite composites are possible by the incorporation of magnetic powders in various elastomer matrices. This modifies the physical properties of the polymer matrix considerably.

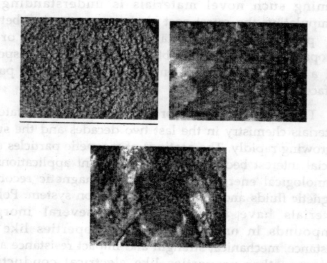

Figure 5. Optical micrograph images of γ-Fe$_2$O$_3$ dispersed (a) natural rubber, (b) polyethylene glycol, (c) polycarbonate composite films.

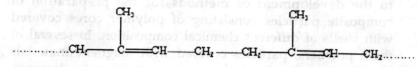

Figure 5(d). Structure of natural rubber. natural rubber. (polyisoprene).

Solvent casting method is one of the easiest methods for the preparation of polymer nanocomposites. It needs simple equipment and is less time consuming. Figures 1 (5-c) show the optical micrograph images of γ-Fe$_2$O$_3$ dispersed natural rubber (γ-Fe$_2$O$_3$ -NR), γ-Fe$_2$O$_3$ dispersed polyethylene glycol (γ-Fe$_2$O$_3$ -PEG) and γ-Fe$_2$O$_3$ dispersed polycarbonate (γ-Fe$_2$O$_3$ - PC), nanocomposite films. The fine dispersion of the magnetite inside the polymer matrix makes it a magnetic polymer. Figure 1(d) shows the structure of the polymer polyisoprene (natural rubber).

Polymer Characterisation

The vigorous development of polymeric science and extensive utilisation of polymeric materials in technology has led in recent years to the increased interest in the preparation and characterisation of polymer and its composite films. Characterisation is an essential part of all investigations dealing with materials.

The important aspects of characterisation are chemical composition and compositional homogeneity (chemical homogeneity), structure (including crystal system where possible atomic coordinates, bonding and ultra structure) and identification and analysis of defects and impurities influencing the properties of the materials. Characterisation, therefore, describes all those features of composition and structure of a material that would suffice for reproducing the material.

The advances made in the last few years in characterisation techniques, especially in the structure elucidation, have been stupendous and have opened new vistas in solid state materials. Among the several characterisation techniques, X-ray diffraction (XRD), scanning electron micrography (SEM) and infrared (IR) spectroscopy are the three important techniques.

X-ray diffraction has played a central role in identifying and characterising solids since the early part of this century. The nature of bonding and the working criteria for distinguishing between short-range and long-range order of crystalline arrangements from the amorphous substances are largely derived from X-ray diffraction and thus it remains as a useful tool to obtain structural information.

X-ray diffraction pattern of amorphous polymer will not show any sharp and highly intensed peaks whereas the nanocomposites of amorphous polymer show sharp and highly intensed peaks. This is due to the development of crystallinity in the amorphous polymer. X-ray diffraction has been most commonly used for routine characterisation as well as for detailed structural elucidation.

Structural phenomena play an important role in determining the properties of a polymer. Mechanical properties are determined not only by the changes in shape confirmation and by motion of individual molecules of the polymers, but by the behaviour of larger and more complex structural formations as well.

The interface boundaries of these formations, known as super molecular structures, are the sites where chemical reactions in the polymer are most likely to begin and centres of crack formation and incipient destruction are likely to arise. It has been found that extensive occurrences of ordered structures are typical not only of crystalline, but also of amorphous polymers. Despite the complex morphology of structural formation in polymers it should not be forgotten that all these structures are built up of separate polymeric molecules.

At a glance it seems self-evident that direct relations must exist between the properties of macromolecules and their ability to form super molecular structures. The shapes of most polymer molecules may vary within wide limits when studying the simplest phenomenon of structure formation. Quite a long time ago it was found that there are two ways by which structures can form. Sufficiently flexible molecules roll up into spherical coil globules, which form in very much the same way as the drops of a liquid under the action of surface tension. But if the macromolecules are sufficiently rigid, the simplest linear structures result. No separate linear polymer molecules have been observed so far. Evidently in majority of cases, they aggregate into chain bunches usually containing several dozen molecules. The phenomenon of structural transformations occurring during deformation is very typical of polymers.

A classic example of structural transformation is the formation of a 'neck' on deformation, described for the case of crystalline polymers some time ago by Kakina. It is also observed in the case of amorphous polymers with developed structures and it is firmly described as a phase transformation. The nature of this phenomenon remained obscure for a long time, but electron microscopy revealed that 'neck' formation is actually a jump wise transition from one super molecular structure to another with a sharp interfacial boundary which is also observed on a microscopic scale.

A well-known example is that of poly(methyl methacrylate) where a sharp boundary can be seen between the isotropic and the oriented parts of the specimen. The formation of a 'neck' on deformation of a large spherulite of isotactic poly (methyl methacrylate) takes place and a sharp boundary can be discerned between the unchanged and the oriented portions of a spherulite.

Figure 6. SEM image of γ-Fe$_2$O$_3$ dispersed natural rubber.

In addition, secondary formations can be seen which have resulted from recrystallisation of the oriented parts, and these are also separated by sharp boundary lines. Figure 6 shows the SEM images of γ-Fe_2O_3 dispersed natural rubber composite. From the figure one can observe the fine dispersion of iron oxide particles in the rubber matrix. The dispersed particles have irregular shape and show agglomeration.

Infrared spectroscopy is one of the most powerful analytical techniques, which offers the possibility of chemical identification. This technique when coupled with intensity measurements may be used for quantitative analysis. One of the important advantages of infrared spectroscopy over the other usual methods of structural analysis (X-ray diffraction, electron spin resonance, etc.) is that it provides information about the structure of a molecule quickly, without tiresome evaluation methods. This method can solve many problems in organic chemistry (polymeric materials) and coordination chemistry, and also advantageously complements the results obtained by other methods. This technique is based upon the simple fact that a chemical substance shows marked selective absorption in the infrared region giving rise to close-packed absorption bands called an IR absorption spectrum, over a wide wavelength range.

Various bands will be present in the IR spectrum, which will correspond to the characteristic functional groups and bonds present in a chemical substance. Thus an IR spectrum of a chemical substance is a fingerprint for its identification. IR spectrum of polymer nanocomposite shows the presence of both nanomaterials and polymers (depending upon the polymer chain) at various frequencies.

Thermal analysis may be defined as the measurement of physical and chemical properties of materials as a function of temperature. The two main thermal analysis techniques are thermogravimetric analysis (TGA) which automatically records the change in weight of a sample as a function of either temperature or time, and the differential thermal analysis (DTA), which measures the difference in temperature, ΔT, between a sample and an inert reference material as a function of temperature; DTA therefore detects change in heat content. A technique closely related but modified to DTA is differential scanning calorimetry (DSC). In DSC, the equipment is designed to allow a quantitative measure of the enthalpy changes, (ΔH), that occurs in a sample as a function of either temperature or time.

DSC is an analytical tool which helps to understand the thermal behaviour of polymer nanocomposites. It helps in finding glass transition temperature (T_g) of polymer and its polymer composites. The increase in T_g values shows the presence of inorganic materials in the polymer matrix. Exciting developments can be expected in the area of polymer nanocomposites and structures in the near future. Investigations on polymer nanocomposite can thus pay rich dividends.

Polymeric Nanostructures

Nanometric structures can be fabricated using techniques such as optical, imprint, scanning-probe, and soft lithographies. Optical lithography techniques are utilised in the production of nanometer-sized features by using exposure radiations in the ultra-violet (UV) region of the electromagnetic spectrum. However, presently, optical lithography is constricted to a minimum feature size of approximately 70 nm; to progress to smaller dimensions, new methods, such as F_2 laser lithography and extreme UV/X-ray lithographies, will have to be developed. Unfortunately, the development of techniques such as these is problematic and embodies the technical challenges inherent in using a resist.

Polymer nanofabrication, based on pattern replication techniques, consists of making a master stamp or mold (hereafter referred to simply as the master) which is then used to replicate superficial nanostructures onto a polymer.

The comparatively low operating costs and low-level complexity of the replication mechanism, the possibility of producing repeatable nanoscale features over a large area, and the fact that a given master can be used several times make polymer nanofabrication appealing with respect to biomedical device applications. In addition, pattern replication techniques are parallel in nature and side-step some of the disadvantages inherent within other forms of lithography. For instance, the resist problems and environmental issues present in optical lithography, such as optical scattering and the disposal of powerful etchant chemicals, are avoided.

Finally, nanostructures can be produced using scanning-probe technologies. This method involves the movement of individual molecules or atoms via scanning-probe microscope cantilever tips. Unfortunately, the linear nature of this technique means that the production of a relatively large structure requires the moving and positioning a large number of building blocks using a single cantilever tip. This takes time, and therefore the replication of large areas of structures using these methods is impractical. However, recent advances towards multiplexing scanning tunnelling microscopy (STM) tips may speed up this technique.

Structural materials for biomedical applications, incorporating nanostructures in this case, need to satisfy a minimum set of requirements. Primarily, the materials need to be biocompatible, i.e., they have to be inert towards the bioanalyte present within the device. Regarding fabrication, the construction materials need to be inexpensive and simple to machine, permitting the production of complex device structures with dimensions ranging from hundreds of microns down to a few tens of nanometers or less. If required, the materials have to be compatible with fluidic applications and provide rigid, smooth surfaces with dimensions relevant to the biological sample. Finally, the materials should preferably be compatible with metallisation technologies, allowing the user to take advantage of non-invasive, electrokinetic manipulation methods and electrical-based analysis techniques. Common structural materials satisfying the above requirements are based on silicon (e.g., pure silicon, glass, or quartz) and on carbon (in the form of polymers and plastics, and, recently, in the development of diamond-based substrates).

Following initial interest in silicon-based substrates; attention is now shifting towards the use of polymers in an effort to exploit their inherent advantages. Apart from the desirable optical and physical properties of polymers, their advantages include the fact that polymers are simple to use: the simplest fabrication technique is merely to pour the polymer onto the substrate, within a suitable container, and then bake to harden the polymer (e.g., polymers such as epoxy resins). Polymer structures are cheaper to produce than silicon-based fabrication technologies, thereby normally dispensing with the need for a high-energy apparatus or time-consuming, multi-step fabrication techniques.

Finally, past experience has enabled scientists to improve on the natural properties of polymers (e.g., flexibility) to produce polymeric structures with properties comparable to their silicon-based counterparts. Fabrication of nanoscale polymeric structures can be achieved using a number of polymer types; most commonly including thermoplastic and elastomeric polymers. Thermoplastic, amorphous polymers are used for imprinting because the viscosity of the polymer is largely dependent on temperature. Near its glass transition temperature (T_g), the polymer softens and can be deformed into the shape of the mold with the help of applied pressure. Room-temperature imprinting can be achieved through careful choice of a polymer with the appropriate melting point and T_g. Polymers are also now being developed with nanofabrication in mind, displaying properties such as higher T_g that are desirable for some nanoimprinting applications. The polymer utilised most frequently in imprinting processes is poly(methylmethacrylate) PMMA. PMMA is an amorphous, thermoplastic polymer with a T_g ~105°C. It is hard and stiff, with low thermal-expansion and pressure-shrinkage coefficients (~5×10^{-5} per °C and ~5×10^{-11} Pa^{-1}, respectively), making it a perfect candidate for imprinting techniques.

PMMA does have the disadvantages of brittleness and notch sensitivity, as well as poor fatigue and solvent resistances. However, this is offset by its optical properties (colourlessness, transparency, and UV resistance), which, together with its excellent optical clarity, make it ideal for use in the production of biomedical apparatuses. For polymer-casting techniques, the polymers need to be elastomeric, which allows them to conform to the superficial structures in the master. A commonly used example of this type of polymer is poly(dimethylsiloxane) PDMS. PDMS is an elastomeric polymer with good thermal stability and homogeneity, characteristics required during the curing step, and it is non-hygroscopic and isotropic. It is a good candidate for the production of apparatus for biomedical applications due to its chemical inertness, durability, and optical transparency down to 300 nm.

Furthermore, it is deformable enough, after curing, to make conformal contact to the surface of a substrate or covering material, greatly facilitating any attempts at bonding to the material. Structures with dimensions greater than 1 μm are easily reproduced, with good resolution using a soft polymer (Young's modulus ~3 MPa), such as

Sylgard 184; however, harder materials (Young's modulus ~10 MPa) are required to achieve optimal resolution. Control of the amount of polymer cross-linking means that the Young's modulus of PDMS can be "tuned" to suit the requirements of the application.

Technologies for Fabrication

Master fabrication

The first step in all replication techniques using polymers consists of fabrication of the master. Available fabrication technologies with nanometer resolution include optical, scanning-probe, and energetic-beam lithographies. These nanometric lithographic techniques are most often used in conjunction with standard microfabrication technologies for the production of micrometer-sized structures within devices. However, the previously mentioned disadvantages of the optical and scanning-probe methods suggests that, at least for the present time, energetic-beam nanofabrication technologies offer the most efficient method of producing masters for replication technologies.

Nanolithographic methods based on energetic beams, for the production of large or complex structures, usually involve long fabrication times (as only a small volume of material is patterned per second) and high equipment/ energy costs (due to the need to form the energetic particle beam under high vacuum conditions), making them impractical for mass production. However, the high-quality nanometric structures (e.g., with aspect ratios of 25 and above) that are produced using these methods make them ideal for the fabrication of masters for replication technologies.

Electron-beam lithography (EBL) is the most common energetic-beam system. The method uses high-energy electrons (100-200 KeV) from a small electron probe (1-10 nm) to write directly onto a photoresist, causing either the breakage or formation of bonds within the resist material. After this patterning, the excess resist is removed using a chemical developer, and the substrate is etched using a chemical etchant. With EBL, trenches down to 30 nm wide (widths down to 7 nm have been reported) can be satisfactorily fabricated, and masters for NIL with comparative dimensions have been produced this way. However, EBL resolution depends heavily on the resist properties, and the resist is often the limiting factor for this technique.

Focused ion beam (FIB) milling can be used to directly remove material from a required substrate. FIB milling is similar to EBL in terms of application; however, there is a fundamental difference between the two techniques. The ions used in FIB consist of charged atomic matter many orders of magnitude more massive than the electrons used in EBL. Thus, the accelerated ion beam can easily be used to dislodge the atoms of the substrate surface and hence mill away unwanted material.

This therefore precludes the need for a resist (and its associated chemistry) as required in EBL. In this way, FIB milling has been used to produce trenches 50 nm deep and ~8 nm in width, and electrodes with a 30-nm spacing. Deep ionbeam lithography is a new technique that can be used to produce 3-D nanostructures and is particularly adept at creating side walls with almost 90° angles and aspect ratios up to 100. By using FIB, masters for imprint technologies containing nanometric dimensioned structures can be fabricated out of materials such as silicon (including silicon dioxide and silicon nitride), metals, and polymers.

Although the FIB technique is most useful as a direct method of nanostructure fabrication, it can also be utilised in the production of structures in conjunction with a resist and for patterning surfaces by ion implantation. FIB can also be used to image surfaces and to machine thin sections of a sample for imaging, while a commercially available FIB apparatus incorporates an inbuilt scanning-electron microscope (SEM) for real-time process imaging. Finally, as an additional technique, FIB can be used to deposit material onto a substrate surface. A gas precursor is introduced into the path of the ion beam, which is then broken down by energetic secondary electrons and deposited on the surface. This deposition can be performed on conducting and insulating substrates alike, which is particularly valuable for the production of electrodes or the protection of samples containing environmentally sensitive materials. The wide range of materials available for etching and deposition makes FIB one of the more versatile apparatuses for nanotechnology production.

Replication techniques

Hot embossing lithography is an imprint technique in which a polymer substrate is imparted with a patterned structure by embossing, using a master, at elevated pressures and temperatures (Fig. 7).

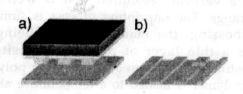

Figure 7. Hot embossing lithography (HEL). (a) The master containing the superficial structures, previously milled in the surface, is pressed into the polymer under temperatures above that of the glass transition temperature (T_g) of the polymer. (b) After a predetermined time period, the temperature is reduced and the pressure is released, allowing the master to be separated from the polymer, revealing the superficial structures replicated in the polymer surface.

The embossing is performed on a press system within which the pressure and temperature can be controlled. Within the press, one surface holds the master, with the negative of the desired pattern on its surface, and the other surface holds a sheet of polymer, such as PMMA. The temperature of both surfaces is increased under vacuum (which helps prevent the formation of air bubbles in the polymer) after which they are brought into contact, and the polymer is embossed at a controlled force for a specified time (Fig. 7a).

To aid in separation of the master and the polymer, while retaining the embossed structure, the temperature is lowered to below that of the Tg of the polymer before removing the embossing force. The master and polymer can then be separated, and a polymer surface containing the required structures, which are the negative of those on the surface of the master, is obtained. The lateral accuracy for the HEL technique is approximately ±3 µm, while height resolution is in the range of tens of nanometers, depending on the applied pressure and temperature.

Like HEL, NIL is a method for replicating structures by means of applied pressure and temperature; but, unlike HEL, it allows replication of nanostructures with both a lateral and a vertical resolution that is well-inside the nanometer range. The imprinting process is similar to that for hot embossing, the main difference being that the substrate is a thin layer of polymer deposited onto a suitable substrate, rather than a freestanding polymer sheet. Again, the polymer is heated to a temperature above its T_g, and elevated pressures, normally higher than those used for HEL, are applied to replicate the nanostructures of the master in the polymer film.

A thin layer of polymer remains within the compressed areas of the polymer, which helps to avoid contact between the master and the substrate, thereby preserving the master and prolonging its life-time. In this way, a master can be used up to ~40 times. An example of the polymers used in NIL is 950k PMMA (PMMA with a molecular weight of 950,000 in anisole solvent), which can be spun onto a suitable substrate. Both thermally and photochemically cross-linkable polymers with low T_g characteristics, and semiconducting polymers have also been evaluated for use in NIL, the latter with a view to the production of organics-based electronics. In NIL, the process time and temperature are dependent on the polymerisation rate of the polymer.

The substrate and the master tend to be the same material in order to avoid the problem of different temperature dependent expansion rates between the two pieces during the imprint process. It is worth mentioning that the imprinting step in NIL is often used as the first step of a pattern-transfer process onto a suitable substrate, or in the fabrication of electrodes.

Subsequently, metal deposition, anisotropic etching, and lift-off processes are used to produce the final structure. Note that, in this case, the final structure is not fabricated from polymer, but from materials such as silicon or metal. NIL has been used to produce 10-nm-wide PMMA structures, and 100-nm-wide trenches, with a spacing of 300 nm, over a 6-inch silicon-wafer substrate. One of the problems that may occur in HEL and NIL is adhesion between the master and the polymer being imprinted.

Avoiding this problem requires prior knowledge of the physics of adhesion in order to guide the choice of suitable material combinations for the master and the polymer. To avoid sticking, the material from which the master is made should be hydrophobic, for example, silicon nitride or nickel. Careful control of the imprinting conditions, such as by releasing the imprinting force at temperatures close to the T_g of the polymer, will also help to eliminate sticking problems. If sticking still occurs between the master and the polymer, anti-sticking layers can be applied, in which materials such as halogenated silanes or PTFE are deposited on the master from the vapour phase via room-temperature adsorption or plasma-deposition techniques. These materials increase the hydrophobicity of the master surface, reducing the possibility of adhesion to the polymer; however, they also increase the complexity of the fabrication technique and thus are used as a last resort.

Production of device

After production of the master using lithographic techniques, polymeric devices can be fabricated using a combination of the above-described methods. The master can be formed in one of two ways (Fig. 8): (1) the superficial features can be machined so that they are below the substrates surface (a negative stamp; Fig. 8a), or (2) they can protrude above the surface of the substrate (a positive stamp; Fig. 8b). The former method has the advantage that less material needs to be removed from the master, reducing its fabrication time. Using these masters to perform a single lithography step produces structures in the polymer that are reversed with respect to the primary master.

Performing a subsequent step, such as polymer casting replication using the first polymer replica as a secondary master, produces superficial structures with the same orientation as the original, primary master. Therefore the fabrication protocol can be designed, depending on the required replica topography (positive or negative), so as to minimise the time and expense required to produce the primary master (which is usually the most time-consuming/expensive step). Often, once fabricated, a polymeric structure needs to be sealed, e.g., for fluidic applications, as much to prevent evaporation of the nanoliter amounts of solvents as to keep them confined within the device structure.

3

Artificial Nonostructures

Each strand of the DNA is about 2 nm wide and composed of a linear chain of four possible bases (adenine, cytosine, guanine, and thymine) on a backbone of alternating sugar molecules and phosphate ions. Each unit of a phosphate, a sugar molecule, and base is called a nucleotide and is about 0.34 nm long. The specific binding through hydrogen bonds between adenine (A) and thymine (T), and cytosine (C) and guanine (G) can result in the joining of two complementary singlestranded DNA to form a doublestranded DNA.

There are two hydrogen bonds between A-T pairs and three hydrogen bonds between G-C pairs. The phosphate ion carries a negative charge in the DNA molecule, which results in electrostatic repulsion of the two strands. In order to keep the two strands together, positive ions must be present in the solution to keep the negative charges neutralised. The joining of two complementary single strands of DNA through hydrogen bonding to form a doublestranded DNA is called hybridisation. If a doublestranded DNA is heated above a certain temperature, the two strands will start to dehybridise and eventually separate into single strands.

The centre temperature of this transition is called the melting temperature, Tm, which is a sensitive function of environmental conditions such as ionic strength, pH, and solvent conditions. As the temperature is reduced, the two strands will eventually come together by diffusion and rehybridise to form the doublestranded structure. These properties of the DNA can be utilised in the ordering and assembly of artificial structures if these structures can be attached to DNA. The first step toward DNA-based nanotechnology is to attach DNA molecules to surfaces. So far, the most widely used attachment scheme utilises the covalent bond between sulphur and gold.

Nuzzo and Allara first reported the formation of long chain ω-substituted dialkyldisulphide molecules on a gold substrate. Bain et al. demonstrated a model system consisting of long-chain thiols that adsorb from solution onto gold to form densely packed, oriented monolayers.

The bonding of the sulphur head group to the gold substrate is in the form of a metal thiolate, which is a very strong bond (~ 44 kcal/mol), and hence the resulting films are quite stable and very suitable for surface attachment of functional groups. The DNA molecule can be functionalised with a thiol (S-H) or a disulphide (S-S) group at the 3' or 5' end. Hickman et al. also demonstrated the selective and orthogonal self-assembly of disulphide with gold and isocyanide with platinum. It should be noted that there are also other strategies to attach DNA to surfaces, for example, the covalent binding of DNA oligonucleotides to a preactivated particle surface and adsorption of biotinylated oligonucleotides on a particle surface coated with avidin. These attachment schemes have served as the fundamental base for DNA-related self-assembly of artificial nanostructures.

DNA-based Nanostructures

There has been a tremendous interest in recent years to develop concepts and approaches for self-assembled systems. While significant work continues along this direction, it has also been recognised that the exquisite molecular recognition of various natural biological materials can be used to form a complex network of potentially useful particles for a variety of optical, electronic, and sensing applications.

This approach can be considered a bottom-up approach rather than the top-down approach of conventional scaling. DNA is a particularly promising candidate to serve as a construction material in nanotechnology. Despite its simplicity, the highly specific Watson-Crick hydrogen bonding allows convenient programming of artificial DNA receptor moieties. The power of DNA as a molecular tool is enhanced by automated methods and by the PCR technique to amplify any DNA sequence from microscopic to macroscopic quantities.

Another attractive feature of DNA is the great mechanical rigidity of short double helices, so that they behave effectively like a rigid rod spacer between two tethered functional molecular components on both ends. Moreover, DNA displays a relatively high physicochemical stability. Finally, nature provides a complete toolbox of highly specific enzymes that enable the processing of the DNA material with atomic precision and accuracy. Seeman and co-workers were the first to exploit DNA's molecular recognition properties to design complex mesoscopic structures based solely on DNA. In their work, branched DNA was used to form stick figures by properly choosing the sequence of the complementary strands. Macrocycles, DNA quadrilateral, DNA knots, Holliday junctions, and other structures were designed.

The same group also reported the design of two-dimensional crystalline forms of DNA double crossover molecules that are programmed to self-assemble by the complementary binding of the sticky ends of the DNA molecules. These lattices can also serve as scaffolding material for other biological materials.

Other researchers also have put effort on using DNA to design complex architectures. Bergstrom and co-workers have designed rigid tetrahedral linkers with arylethynylaryl spacers to direct the assembly of attached oligonucleotide linker arms into novel DNA macrocycles. Unlike Seeman's approach where the DNA serves as both the vertices and the edges of the assembled architectures, Bergstrom's approach utilises rigid tetrahedral organic vertices, where the attached oligonucleotides serve as the connectors for the design of more complex architectures. In principle, a variable number of oligonucleotide arms could be attached to the core tetrahedral organic linkers, thereby allowing for the construction of different types of DNA structures.

In 1996, Mirkin and co-workers first described a method of assembling colloidal gold nanoparticles into macroscopic aggregates using DNA as linking elements. This process could also be reversed when the temperature was increased due to the melting of the DNA oligonucleotides. Because of the molecular recognition properties associated with the DNA interconnects, this strategy allows one to control interparticle distance, strength of the particle interconnects, and size and chemical identity of the particles in the targeted macroscopic structure.

In the same time, Alivisatos et al. also reported DNA-based techniques to organise gold nanocrystals into spatially defined structures. In their work, gold particles were attached to either the 3' or 5' end of 19 nucleotide long singlestranded DNA molecules through the well-known thiol attachment scheme. Then, 37 nucleotide long singlestranded DNA template molecules were added to the solution containing the gold nanoparticles functionalised with singlestranded DNA. The authors showed that the nanocrystals could be assembled into dimers (parallel and antiparallel) and trimers upon hybridisation of the DNA molecules with that of the template molecule. Due to the ability to choose the number of nucleotides, the gold particles can be placed at defined positions from each other.

Based on the work of Alivisatos and co-workers, Loweth et al. have studied further details of the formation of the hetero-dimeric and hetero-trimeric nonperiodic nanocluster molecules. They showed exquisite control of the placement of 5 nm and 10 nm gold nanoclusters that were derivatised with singlestranded DNA. Various schemes of hetero-dimers and hetero-trimers were designed and demonstrated with TEM images. Mucic et al. have made the construction of binary nanoparticle networks composed of 9 nm particles and 31 nm particles, both composed of citrate-stabilised colloidal gold.

These 9 and 31 nm particles are coated with different 12-mer oligonucleotides via a thiol bond. When a third DNA sequence (24-mer), which is complementary to the oligonucleotides on both particles is added, hybridisation led to the association of particles. When the ratio of 9 nm to 31 nm particles is large, a binary assembly of the nanoparticles is formed. Maeda et al. recently reported two-dimensional assembly of Au nanoparticles with a DNA network template.

First, a gold nanoparticle is attached to a DNA1 molecule through the Au-thiol reaction. The DNA1 molecule is then hybridised with a DNA2 molecule possessing a counterbase sequence. Finally, the components are built into a DNA network consisting of DNA3 through the hybridisation of DNA2 and DNA3. As a consequence, the Au particles are inserted into the DNA3 network template.

Many strategies have been used to synthesise semiconductor particles and particle arrays. Coffer and co-workers were the first to utilise DNA as a stabiliser/template to form both CdS nanoparticles and mesoscopic aggregates from them. Their original efforts were based on the use of linear duplexes of DNA in solution as a stabiliser for forming CdS nanoparticles. The initial results indicated that CdS nanoparticles could be formed from Cd^{2+} and S^{2-} in the presence of DNA. However, the role of DNA in the formation of the nanoparticles and the interactions between DNA and the particles after their formation were not clarified. Further studies demonstrated that DNA base sequence, and more specifically the content of the base adenine, had a significant effect on the size of the CdS particles formed and their resulting photophysical properties.

In order to form well-defined mesoscale structures in solution, Coffer and co-workers developed a new strategy for binding a template DNA strand to a solid substrate. This approach provides many possibilities for synthesising mesoscale structures since particle composition, shape, length, and sequence of the DNA template can be controlled.

The main drawback of this approach is the difficulty of forming monodispersed nanoparticle samples since the nature of the DNA/Cd^{2+} interactions is poorly understood. In addition, the relative spacing and orientation of the resulting nanoparticles within the mesostructure are difficult to control, and consequently, tailoring and predicting the resulting properties of the materials is problematic. Torimoto et al. tried another approach to assemble CdS nanoparticle using DNA.

The idea is to use the electrostatic interaction between the cationic surface modifiers on the CdS nanoparticles and the phosphate groups in DNA double strands. Mitchell et al. used thiolated oligonucleotides to partially displace mercaptopropionic acid molecules from the surface of the dots. However, the presence of carboxyl groups on the surface of the nanocrystals was found to cause strong nonspecific binding to the oligonucleotides probe backbone. To overcome this problem, Pathal et al. developed a strategy in which hydroxylated CdSe/ZnS nanocrystals were covalently attached to oligonucleotide sequences via a carbamale linkage.

Tour and co-workers taken an approach similar to that of Coffer in using DNA to assemble DNA/fullerene hybrid organic materials. In their strategy, the negative phosphate backbone of DNA was used as a template to bind and organise C_{60} fullerene molecules modified with a N,N-dimethylpyrrolidinium iodide moiety into defined mesoscopic architectures.

The concept of DNA-mediated self-assembly of nanostructures has also been extended to metallic nanowires. Braun et al. have utilised DNA as a template to grow conducting silver nanowires. Two gold electrodes separated by a defined distance (12-16 µm) were deposited onto a glass slide using photolithography. The gold electrodes subsequently were modified with noncomplementary hexane disulphide modified oligonucleotides through well-established thiol adsorption chemistry on Au. Subsequently, a fluorescently labelled strand of DNA containing sticky ends that are complementary to the oligonucleotides attached to the electrodes is introduced.

Hybridisation of the fluorescently tagged DNA molecule to the surface-confined alkylthiololigonucleotides was confirmed by fluorescence microscopy, which showed a fluorescent bridge connecting the two electrodes. After a single DNA bridge was observed, the excess hybridisation reagents were removed. Silver ions then were deposited onto the DNA through cation exchange with sodium and complexation with the DNA bases. This process can be followed by monitoring the quenching of the fluorescent tag on the DNA by the Ag ions. After almost complete quenching of the fluorescence, the silver ion bound to the template DNA is reduced using standard hydroquinone reduction procedures to form small silver aggregates along the backbone of the DNA. A continuous silver wire is then formed by further Ag ion deposition onto the previously constructed silver aggregates followed by reduction. The wires are comprised of 30-50 nm Ag grains that are contiguous along the DNA backbone.

Two terminal electrical measurements subsequently were performed on the Ag wire depicted in the AFM image. When the current-voltage characteristics of the Ag wire were monitored, no current was observed at near zero bias (10 V in either scan direction), indicating an extremely high resistance. At a higher bias, the wire becomes conductive. Surprisingly, the current-voltage characteristics were dependent on the direction of the scan rate, yielding different I-V curves. Although not well understood, it was postulated that the individual Ag grains that comprise the Ag nanowires may require simultaneous charging, or Ag corrosion may have occurred, resulting in the high resistance observed at low bias.

By depositing more silver and thereby growing a thicker Ag nanowire, the nocurrent region was reduced from 10 V to 0.5 V, demonstrating crude control over the electrical properties of these systems. In addition, control experiments where one of the components (DNA or Ag) was removed from the assembly produced no current, establishing that all of the components are necessary to form the conducting Ag nanowires. This work is a proof-of-concept demonstration of how DNA can be used in a new type of chemical lithography to guide the formation of nanocircuitry. Martin et al. also reported the fabrication of Au and Ag wires using the DNA as a template or skeleton. The basic idea behind this work is to fabricate gold or platinum metal wires, functionalise these wires with exchange and formation of complexes between the gold and the DNA bases. Current voltage characteristics were measured to demonstrate the possible use of these nanowires.

The authors also reported the formation of luminescent self-assembled poly (p-phenylene vinylene) wires for possible optical applications. The work has a lot of potential and much room for further research to control the wire width, the contact resistances between the gold electrode and the silver wires, and use of other metals and materials. More recently, Yan et al. demonstrated the design and construction of a DNA nanostructure that has a square aspect ratio and readily self-assembles into two distinct lattice forms: nanoribbons and two-dimensional nanogrids. The 4×4 tile contains four four-arm DNA branched junctions pointing in four directions. Such nanogrids have a large cavity size, which may serve as binding or tethering sites for other molecular components.

The loops at the centre of each 4×4 tile can be modified with appropriate functional groups and for used as a scaffold for directing periodic assembly of desired molecules. Periodic protein arrays were achieved by templated self-assembly of streptavidin onto the DNA nanogrids. The authors also used the 4×4 tile assemblies as templates to construct a highly conductive, uniform-width silver nanowire. A twoterminal I-V measurement of the resulting silver nanowire was conducted at room temperature.

In addition to using DNA, there are also reports on using other biomolecules to fabricate nanowires. Djalali et al. recently developed a new biological approach to fabricate Au nanowires using sequenced peptide nanotubes as templates. Briefly, Au ions are captured by imidazole and amine groups of the sequenced peptides on the nanotubes, and then the trapped Au ions in the peptides nucleate into Au nanocrystals after reducing those ions by hydrazine hydrate. This approach has potential to control the size and the packing density of the Au nanocrystals by simply adjusting external experimental conditions such as pH, temperature, and ion concentration.

Single-walled carbon nanotubes (SWNT) are composed of a single layer of graphene sheet rolled-up into a cylinder, with diameters in the range 1-2 nm. Since the discovery of single-walled carbon nanotubes, this new class of materials has demonstrated great potential to make a major contribution to a variety of nanotechnology applications, including molecular electronics, hydrogen storage media, and scanning probe microscope tips.

Carbon nanotubes can be expected to provide a basis for a future generation of nanoscale devices, and it has been predicted that modification of SWNT will lead to an even more diverse range of applications. For example, the electrical properties of empty SWNT are extremely sensitive to their structure and the existence of defects, which imposes great difficulty for using unfilled nanotubes in electronic device applications. The property of filled SWNT, on the other hand, will be dominated by the filling materials, and therefore, filled nanotubes will be more robust in applications such as nanoelectronics.

The unusual physical and chemical properties also depend on the nanotube diameter and helicity. Kiang and co-workers developed an efficient method for catalytic synthesis of SWNTs with a wide range of diameters. Many applications would benefit from the availability of SWNT of varying diameters and helicities. At present, SWNT-based devices are fabricated by "top-down" lithographic methods. The construction of more complex architectures with high device density requires the development of a "bottom-up," massively parallel strategy that exploits the molecular properties of SWNTs.

DNA-guided assembly of carbon nanotubes could be one way toward this aim. Besides, carbon nanotubes have useful properties for various potential applications in biological devices. For instance, nanotubes can be used as electrodes for detecting biomolecules in solutions, similar to commonly used conventional carbon based electrode materials. Also, the electrical properties of SWNTs are sensitive to surface charge transfer and changes in the surrounding electrostatic environment, undergoing drastic changes simply by adsorption of certain molecules or polymers. SWNTs are therefore promising as chemical sensors for detecting molecules in the gas phase and as biosensors for probing biological processes in solutions.

One way to link DNA with nanotubes is via noncovalent interactions. Dai and co-workers described a simple and general approach to noncovalent functionalisation of the sidewalls of SWNTs and subsequent immobilisation of various biological molecules onto nanotubes with a high degree of control and specificity. Their method involves a bifunctional molecule, 1-pyrenebutanoic acid, succinimidyl ester, irreversibly adsorbed onto the inherently hydrophobic surfaces of SWNTs in an organic solvent dimethylformamide (DMF) or methanol.

The pyrenyl group, being highly aromatic in nature, is known to interact strongly with the basal plane of graphite via π-stacking, and also found to strongly interact with the sidewalls of SWNTs in a similar manner, thus providing a fixation point for the biomolecule on the nanotubes. The anchored molecules on SWNTs are highly stable against desorption in aqueous solutions. This leads to the functionalisation of SWNTs with succinimidyl ester groups that are highly reactive to nucleophilic substitution by primary and secondary amines that exist in abundance on the surface of most proteins.

The mechanism of protein immobilisation on nanotubes, then, involves the nucleophilic substitution of N-hydroxysuccinimide by an amine group on the protein, resulting in the formation of an amide bond. This technique enables the immobilisation of a wide range of biomolecules on the sidewalls of SWNTs with high specificity and efficiency.

Meanwhile, people also tried to use covalent chemistry to link DNA with nanotubes because covalent interaction is expected to provide the best stability, accessibility, and selectivity during competitive hybridisation. Hamers and co-workers have developed a multi-step route to the formation of covalently linked adducts of SWNT and DNA oligonucleotides.

Purified SWNTs were oxidised to form carboxylic acid groups at the ends and sidewalls. These were reacted with thionyl chloride and then ethylenediamine to produce amineterminated sites. The amines were then reacted with the heterobifunctional cross-linker succinimidyl 4-(N-maleimidomethyl)cyclohexane-1-carboxylate, (SMCC), leaving the surface terminated with maleimide groups.

Finally, thiol-terminated DNA was reacted with these groups to produce DNA-modified SWNTs. It is found that DNA molecules covalently linked to SWNTs are accessible to hybridisation as evidenced by strong tendency in hybridisation with molecules having complementary sequences compared with noncomplementary sequences. Williams et al. recently developed a way to couple SWNTs covalently to peptide nucleic acid (PNA, an uncharged DNA analogue) and to hybridise these macromolecular wires with complementary DNA.

Dwyer et al. also reported some progress toward the DNA-guided assembly of carbon nanotubes. They used amine-terminated DNA strands to functionalise the open ends and defect sites of single-walled carbon nanotubes. Nguyen et al. developed an approach for the attachment of DNA to oxidatively opened ends of multiwalled carbon nanotube arrays.

In addition to necessary steps such as opening the closed carbon nanotube (CNT) ends and removing metal catalyst at the nanotube tips, a novel and critical step in their approach is the deposition of a spin-on glass (SOG) film inside hydrophobic CNT arrays. It is found that the SOG improves the mechanical rigidity of the CNT array as well as enhances the DNA coupling efficiency.

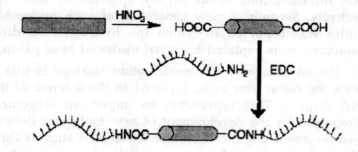

Figure 1. The DNA/nanotube reaction scheme. Capped nanotubes are oxidatively opened and then reacted with amine-terminated single-stranded DNA.

In addition to DNA, there are also plenty of interests in functionalising carbon nanotubes with other biomolecules such as protein, peptide, etc. Pantarotto et al. recently reported the synthesis, structural characterisation, and immunological properties of carbon nanotubes functionalised with peptides.

They employed two different methods to link bioactive peptides to SWNTs through a stable bond: (i) the fragment condensation of fully protected peptides and (ii) selective chemical ligation.

Self-assembly

Among the variety of approaches to DNA-based supramolecular chemistry, the strategy of replacing DNA natural bases by alternative bases that possess distinct shape, size, or function has allowed the modification of DNA in a highly specific and siteselective manner. One good example is the replacement of the natural bases by artificial nucleosides or nucleoside mimics. However, this approach is restricted to molecules with shapes and sizes that are commensurate to normal bases to ensure that the

DNA modifications occur highly specifically and site selectively. Recently, a new generation of such nucleoside mimics was reported in which the hydrogen bonding interactions were replaced by metal-mediated base pairing.

The advantage of this modification strategy is that it allows the metal ions to be replaced in the interior of the DNA duplex. This represents an important structural prerequisite for the development of new molecular devices based on interacting metal centers. Metal ions such as Cu^{2+}, Pd^{2+}, and Ag^+, have been successfully incorporated as artificial DNA bases into oligonucleotides by different groups. Introduction of such metal-induced base pairs into DNA would not only affect the assembly-disassembly processes and the structure of DNA double strands but also confer a variety of metal-based functions upon DNA.

A remarkable consequence of the insertion of just one artificial metal-ion-mediated base pair is that the thermal stability of the modified DNA duplex is strongly enhanced relative to one with normal hydrogen-bond interactions. Tanaka et al. showed that replacement of hydrogen-boned base pairing present in natural DNA by metal-mediated base pairing, with the subsequent arrangement of these metallo-base pairs into a direct stacked contact, could lead -to "metallo-DNA" in which metal ions are lined up along the helix axis in a controlled and stepwise manner. Later, they successfully arranged Cu^{2+} ions into a magnetic chain using the artificial DNA.

The most important structural feature of this artificial DNA is the alignment of the Cu^{2+} ions along the axes inside the duplexes. The canonical helical conformation of these DNA-like duplexes ensures regular Cu^{2+}-Cu^{2+} distances. From EPR signals the distance in the artificial DNA duplexes was estimated to be 3.7Å, which is remarkably similar to the distance between two adjacent base pairs in natural DNA duplexes (3.4Å).

Nanomaterials as Novel Biosensors

In recent years, there have been significant interests in using novel solid-state nanomaterials for biological and medical applications. The unique physical properties of nanoscale solids (dots or wires) in conjunction with the remarkable recognition capabilities of biomolecules could lead to miniature biological electronics and optical devices including probes and sensors. Such devices may exhibit advantages over existing technology not only in size but also in performance. Sequence-specific DNA detection is an important topic because of its application in the disgnosis of pathogenic and genetic diseases.

Many detection techniques have been developed that rely upon target hybridisation with radioactive, fluorescent, chemiluminescent, or other types of labelled probes. Moreover, there are indirect detection methods that rely on enzymes to generate colorimetric, fluorescent, or chemiluminescent signals.

Mirkin and co-workers developed a novel method for detecting polynucleotides using gold nanoparticle probes. Their method utilises the distance- and size-dependent optical properties of aggregated Au nanoparticles functionalised with 5'-(alkanethiol)-capped oligonucleotides. Introduction of a singlestranded target oligonucleotide (30 bases) into a solution containing the appropriate probes resulted in the formation of a polymeric network of nanoparticles with a concomitant red-to-pinkish/purple colour change.

Hybridisation was facilitated by annealing and melting of the solutions, and the denaturation of these hybrid materials showed transition temperatures over a narrow range that allowed differentiation of a variety of imperfect targets. Transfer of the hybridisation mixture to a reverse-phase silica plate resulted in a blue colour upon drying that could be detected visually.

The unoptimised system can detect about 10 femtomoles of an oligonucleotide. This method has many desirable features including rapid detection, a colorimetric response, good selectivity, and a little or no required instrumentation. Later, the same group reported a related method in which the Au nanoparticles functionalised with 5'- and 3'-(alkanethiol)-capped oligonucletides that causes a tail-to-tail alignment of Au nanoparticle probes. This new system exhibits extraordinary selectivity and provides a simple means for colorimetric, one-pot detection of a target oligonucleotide in the presence of a mixture of oligonucleotides with sequences differing by a single nucleotide.

Maxwell et al. also reported that biomolecules and nanoparticles can be both structurally and functionally linked to create a new class of nanobiosensors that is able to recognise and detect specific DNA sequences and single-base mutations in a homogeneous format. Oligonucleotide molecules labelled with a thiol group are attached at one end of the core and a fluorophore at the other end. This hybrid construct is found to spontaneously assemble into a constrained arch-like conformation on the particle surface. In the assembled state, the fluorophore is quenched by the nanoparticle. Upon target binding, the constrained conformation opens and the fluorophore leaves the surface because of the structural rigidity of the hybridised DNA (doublestranded), and fluorescence is restored. This structural change generates a fluorescence signal that is highly sensitive and specific to the target DNA.

Cao et al. have also developed a nanoparticle-based method for DNA and RNA detection in which Au nanoparticle probes are labelled with oligonucleotides and Ramanactive dyes. The gold particles form a template for silver reduction, and the silver coating acts as a surface-enhanced Raman scattering promoter for the dye-labelled particles that have been captured by target molecules and an underlying chip in microarray format. Compared with fluorescencebased chip detection, this nanoparticle-based methodology offers several advantages.

The ratio of Raman intensities can be extracted from a single Raman spectrum with singlelaser excitation. Second, the number of available Raman dyes is much greater than the number of available and discernable fluorescent dyes. Therefore, this method offers potentially greater flexibility, a larger pool of available and nonoverlapping probes, and higher multiplexing capabilities than do conventional fluorescence-based detection approaches.

A major challenge in the area of DNA detection is the development of methods that do not rely on polymerase chain reaction or comparable target-amplification systems that require additional instrumentation and reagents. Park et al. reported an electrical method for DNA detection. They find that the binding of oligonucleotides functionalised with gold nanoparticles leads to conductivity changes associated with target-probe binding events.

The binding events localise gold nanoparticles in an electrode gap; silver deposition facilitated by these nanoparticles bridges the gap and leads to readily measurable conductivity changes. With this method, they have detected target DNA at concentration as low as 500 femtomolar with a point mutation selectivity factor of ~ 100,000:1. Wang et al. reported a nanoparticle-based protocol for detecting DNA hybridisation.

The idea is based on a magnetically induced solid-state electrochemical stripping detection of metal tags. Their approach involves the hybridisation of a target oligonucleotide to probe-coated magnetic beads, followed by binding of the streptavidincoated gold nanoparticles to the captured target, catalytic silver precipitation on the gold particle tags, a magnetic collection of the DNA-linked particle assembly and solid-state stripping detection.

The DNA hybrid bridges the metal nanoparticles to the magnetic beads, with multiple duplex links per particle. Most of the three-dimensional DNA-linked aggregate is covered with silver following the catalytic precipitation of silver on gold.

Such DNA-linked particle assembly can thus be collected magnetically and anchored onto the thick-film working electrode. This leads to a direct contact of the silver with the surface and enables the solid-state electrochemical transduction. Weizmann et al. also emploied nucleic acid-functionalised magnetic particles for amplified DNA sensing and immunosensing.

Amine-functionalised borosilicate-based magnetic particles were modified with DNA 1 using the heteronifunctional corss-linker 3-maleimidopropionic acid N-hydroxysuccinimide ester. The probe 1 is complementary to a part of the target sequence 2.

The 1-functionalised magnetic particles are hybridised in a single step with a mixture that includes the target 2 and the biotin-labelled nucleic acid 3 that is complementary to the free segment of 2. The three-component doublestranded DNA assembly is then interacted with avidin-horseradish peroxidase (HRP) that act as a biocatalytic label.

The DNA/avidin-HPR-functionalised magnetic particles are subsequently mixed with magnetic particles modified with the naphthoquinone unit 4. The mixture of the magnetic particles is then attracted to the electrode supported by means of an external magnet. Electrochemical reduction of the naphthoquinone to the respective hydroquinone results in the catalysed reduction of O_2 to H_2O_2.

The electrogenerated H_2O_2 leads, in the presence of luminal 5 and the enzyme label HRP, to the generation of the chemiluminescence signal. The chemiluminescence occurs only when the target DNA 2 is in the analysed sample. Furthermore, the light intensity relates directly to the number of recognition pairs of 1 and 2 associated with the electrode, and thus it provides a quantitative measure of the concentration of 2 in the sample.

The subsequent rotation of the particles on the surface by means of the rotating external magnet results in the enhanced electrogenerated chemiluminescence, because the magnetic particle behave as rotating microelectrode, where the interaction of O_2 and luminal with the catalysts on the electrode is controlled by convection rather than by diffusion. Thus, the rotation of the magnetic particles yields amplified detection of DNA. He et al. recently described a new approach for ultrasensitive detection of DNA hybridisation based on nanoparticle-amplified surface plasmon resonance (SPR). Use of the Au nanoparticle tags leads to a greater than 10-fold increase in angle shift, which corresponds to a more than 1000-fold improvement in sensitivity for the target oligonucleotide as compared to the unamplified binding event.

This enhanced shift in SPR reflectivity is a combined result of greatly increased surface mass, high dielectric constant of Au particles, and electromagnetic coupling between Au nanoparticles and the Au film. DNA melting and digestion experiments further supported the feasibility of this approach in DNA hybridisation studies. The extremely large angle shifts observed in particle-amplified SPR make it possible to conduct SPR imaging experiments on DNA arrays.

The sensitivity of this technique begins to approach that of traditional fluorescence-based methods for DNA hybridisation. These results illustrate the potential of particle-amplified SPR for array-based DNA analysis and ultrasensitive detection of oligonucleotides. Su et al. demonstrated a microcantilever based mechanical resonance DNA detection using gold nanoparticle-modified probes. The core idea is to measure the mass change of a microfabricated cantilever induced by DNA hybridisation through the shift of the resonance frequency of the cantilever.

The hybridisation is reflected by the attachment of gold nanoparticles on the cantilever and then chemically amplified by gold nanoparticle-catalysed nucleation of silver in a developing solution. The authors claim that this method can detect target DNA at a concentration of 0.05 nM or lower. When combined with stringent washing, this technique can detect a single base pair mismatched DNA strand. The cantilever is 1/100 times smaller than its macroscopic quartz crystal microbalance counterpart, and it can be mass-produced as miniaturised sensor arrays by current processing technology.

Multiple DNA detection is also possible by coating multiple cantilevers with various capture DNA strands and monitoring the change in their resonance frequencies. Nanoparticle-based biosensors can also be used for the physical and chemical manipulation of biological systems. Hamad-Schifferli et al. recently demonstrated remote control of the hybridisation behaviour of DNA molecules by inductive coupling of a radio-frequency magnetic field to a Au nanocrystal covalently linked to DNA. When the magnetic field is on, the inductive coupling to the Au nanocrystal increases the local temperature of the bound DNA, thereby inducing denaturation while leaving surrounding molecules relatively unaffected.

Removing the field restores the hybridisation of DNA. Because dissolved biomolecules dissipate heat in less than 50 picoseconds, the switch is fully reversible. This concept shows promising potential for the control of hybridisation and other biological functions on the molecular scale. There are also intense studies on semiconductor quantum dots conjugated with biomolecules as novel probes. These nanometer-sized conjugates are watersoluble and biocompatible, and provide important advantages over organic dyes and lanthanide probes. In particular, the emission wavelength of quantum-dot nanocrystals can be continuously tuned by changing the particle size, and a single light source can be used for simultaneous excitation of all different-sized dots. High-quality dots are also highly stable against photobleaching and have narrow, symmetric emission spectra. These novel optical properties render quantum dots ideal fluorophores for ultrasensitive, multicolour, and multiplexing applications in molecular biotechnology and bioengineering.

Melting Properties

The UV-visible spectrum is also used to monitor the melting properties of the DNA-linked aggregates. The DNA double helix has a smaller extinction coefficient than does singlestranded DNA due to hypocromism, and, therefore, the absorption intensity at 260 nm increases as a result of DNA melting. Meanwhile, the melting will also cause sharp changes in the gold nanoparticle extinction coefficient due to the dissociation of the aggregate. Therefore, the melting can be monitored at either 260 nm or 520 nm as a function of temperature. The 260 and 520 nm melting curves are very similar, indicating that DNA and gold nanoparticle melting are closely correlated.

The transition width as well as the melting temperature has been dramatically modified by the binding to gold particles. It is also clear that the melting properties are highly dependent on the gold nanoparticle size. For bigger gold particles the melting temperature is higher.

Besides the particle size, the melting properties of DNA-linked gold nanoparticles are also strongly dependent on other variables, including the DNA density on the gold surface, the interparticle distance, and the salt concentration in the solution. Jin et al. recently performed a series of experiments to systematically study the effects of various external variables.

A high DNA surface density on the Au nanoparticle is expected to provide advantage in particle stabilisation as well as to increase the hybridisation efficiency. Experimental results show that for temperature below 70°C, the melting temperature is proportional to the DNA surface density when the nanoparticle and target concentrations are kept constant. Also, a slight broadening of the melting transition was observed as the DNA density decreases. The interparticle distance is another key parameter to control the melting properties.

As gold nanoparticles are linked together via DNA hybridisation, electromagnetic coupling between the nanoparticles result in significant damping of their surface plasmon resonances. The amount of extinction due to scattering is also influenced by the interparticle spacing. Interparticle distance also influences van der Waals and electrostatic forces between the particles, weakly affecting duplex DNA stability and hybridisation/dehybridisation properties.

Experimental results show that the melting temperature increases with the length of the interparticle distance for temperatures below 70°C, and there is a linear relationship between the two. The melting behaviour of DNA-linked nanoparticle aggregation also depends on the salt concentration. In Jin et al's study, the melting temperature increased from 41 to 61.5°C as the salt concentration was increased from 0.05 to 1.0 M while keeping the nanoparticle and linker DNA concentration constant.

Moreover, increasing salt concentration also causes larger aggregates as evidenced by a larger absorption change during melting. It is believed that the salt brings about a screening effect that minimises electrostatic repulsion between the DNA-DNA bases and between the nanoparticles, hence, strengthening the effect of the linker

4
Nanotube Technologies

There are many types of nanotube, from various inorganic kinds, such as those made from boron nitride, to organic ones, such as those made from self-assembling cyclic peptides (protein components) or from naturally-occurring heat shock proteins (extracted from bacteria that thrive in extreme environments). However, carbon nanotubes excite the most interest, promise the greatest variety of applications, and currently appear to have by far the highest commercial potential. They are in fact a hugely varied range of structures, with similarly huge variations in properties and ease of production.

Adding to the confusion is the existence of long, thin, and often hollow, carbon fibers that have been called carbon nanotubes but have a quite different make-up from that of the nanotubes that scientists generally refer to. Carbon nanotubes were 'discovered' in 1991 by Sumio Iijima of NEC and are effectively long, thin cylinders of graphite, which you will be familiar with as the material in a pencil or as the basis of some lubricants. Graphite is made up of layers of carbon atoms arranged in a hexagonal lattice, like chicken wire in Figure 1.

Though the chicken wire structure itself is very strong, the layers themselves are not chemically bonded to each other but held together by weak forces called Van der

Waals. It is the sliding across each other of these layers that gives graphite its lubricating qualities and makes the mark on a piece of paper as you draw your pencil over it. Now imagine taking one of these sheets of chicken wire and rolling it up into a cylinder and joining the loose wire ends.

The result is a tube that was once described by Richard Smalley (who shared the Nobel Prize for the discovery of a related form of carbon called buckminsterfullerene) as "in one direction . . . the strongest damn thing you'll ever make in the universe". In addition to their remarkable strength, which is usually quoted as 100 times that of steel at one-sixth of the weight, carbon nanotubes have shown a surprising array of other properties. They can conduct heat as efficiently as most diamond, conduct electricity as efficiently as copper, yet also be semiconducting.

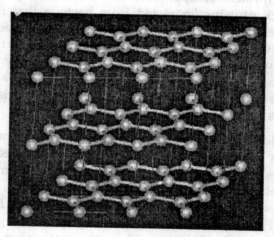

Figure 1. Layer structure of graphite

They can produce streams of electrons very efficiently, which can be used to create light in displays for televisions or computers, or even in domestic lighting, and they can enhance the fluorescence of materials they are close to. Their electrical properties can be made to change in the presence of certain substances or as a result of mechanical stress. Nanotubes within nanotubes can act like miniature springs and they can even be stuffed with other materials. Nanotubes and their variants hold promise for storing fuels such as hydrogen or methanol for use in fuel cells and they make good supports for catalysts.

One of the major classifications of carbon nanotubes is into single-walled varieties (SWNTs), which have a single cylindrical wall, and multi-walled varieties (MWNTs), which have cylinders within cylinders. The lengths of both types vary greatly, depending on the way they are made, and are generally microscopic rather than nanoscopic, i.e. greater than 100 nanometers (a nanometer is a millionth of a millimetre). The aspect ratio (length divided by diameter) is typically greater than 100 and can be up to 10,000, but recently even this was made to look small.

Single-Walled Carbon Nanotubes (SWNTs)

These are the stars of the nanotube world, and somewhat reclusive ones at that, being much harder to make than the multi-walled variety. The oft-quoted amazing properties generally refer to SWNTs. They are basically tubes of graphite and are normally capped at the ends, although the caps can be removed. The caps are made by mixing in some pentagons with the hexagons and are the reason that nanotubes are considered close cousins of buckminsterfullerene (Figure 2), a roughly spherical molecule made of sixty carbon atoms, that looks like a soccer ball and is named after the architect Buckminster Fuller.

The theoretical minimum diameter of a carbon nanotube is around 0.4 nanometers, which is about as long as two silicon atoms side by side, and nanotubes this size have been made. Average diameters tend to be around the 1.2 nanometer mark, depending on the process used to create them. SWNTs are more pliable than their multi-walled counterparts and can be twisted, flattened and bent into small circles or around sharp bends without breaking.

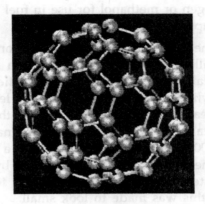

Figure 2. Buckminsterfullerene.

There are various ways of producing SWNTs. The detailed mechanisms responsible for nanotube growth are still not fully understood and computer modelling is playing an increasing role in fathoming the complexities. The ambition of SWNT producers is to gain greater control over their diameters, lengths, and other properties, such as chirality.

The volumes of SWNTs produced are currently small and the quality and purity are variable. Carbon Nanotechnologies Inc. of Houston, Texas, are currently ramping up production to a half a kilogram a day, which is actually huge in comparison to amounts of SWNTs that have been made historically. Various companies pursuing specific nanotube applications produce their own material in house.

Imagine again the chicken wire that we roll up to make the nanotube. In fact, imagine a chicken wire fence out of which will be cut a rectangle to roll into a tube. You could cut the rectangle with the sides vertical or at various angles. Additionally, when joining the sides together, you can raise or lower one side. In some cases it will not be possible to make a tube such that the loose ends match and hexagons are formed, but in other cases it will, and these represent the possible permutations of SWNTs (Figure 3). The possibilities are two forms in which a pattern circles around the diameter of the tube, often called zigzag and armchair, and a variety of forms in which the hexagons spiral up or down the tube with varying steepness, these being the chiral forms. There is theoretically an infinite variety of the latter, if you allow for infinite diameters of nanotubes.

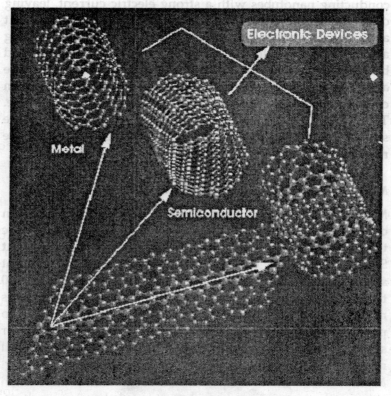

Figure 3. Schematic representation of rolling graphite to create a carbon nanotube

Which of these forms a nanotube takes is the major determinant of its electrical properties, i.e. whether the tube is semiconducting or conducting. For a long time, the fact that all known production methods created a mix of types has been considered one of the hurdles to be overcome if the electronic properties are to be exploited.

Claims have now been made that it is possible to produce only the semiconducting kind. Additionally, there are approaches that can yield only semiconducting nanotubes from a mix of semiconducting and conducting ones. One such approach relies on vaporizing the conducting nanotubes with a strong electric current, leaving only the semiconducting kind behind. A more recent approach is simply to leave the mix of nanotubes lying around for a while-the metallic ones are oxidised and become semiconducting. In the early part of 2001 there were also reports that nanotubes had been induced to form crystals, each of which contained just one type of nanotube. This would have been a nice separation method but the silence on this approach since then suggests that these results have not been duplicated.

Multi-Walled Carbon Nanotubes (MWNTs)

Multi-walled carbon nanotubes are basically like Russian dolls made out of SWNTs-concentric cylindrical graphitic tubes. In these more complex structures, the different SWNTs that form the MWNT may have quite different structures (length and chirality). MWNTs are typically 100 times longer than they are wide and have outer diameters mostly in the tens of nanometers. Although it is easier to produce significant quantities of MWNTs than SWNTs, their structures are less well understood than single-wall nanotubes because of their greater complexity and variety. Multitudes of exotic shapes and arrangements, often with imaginative names such as bamboo-trunks, sea urchins, necklaces or coils, have also been observed under different processing conditions. The variety of forms may be interesting but also has a negative side-MWNTs always have more defects than SWNTs and these diminish their desirable properties.

Many of the nanotube applications now being considered or put into practice involve multi-walled nanotubes, because they are easier to produce in large quantities at a reasonable price and have been available in decent amounts for much longer than SWNTs. In fact one of the major manufacturers of MWNTs at the moment, Hyperion Catalysis, does not even sell the nanotubes directly but only pre-mixed with polymers for composites applications.

The tubes involved typically have 8 to 15 walls and are around 10 nanometres wide and 10 micrometers long. Other companies are moving into this space, notably formidable players like Mitsui, with plans to produce similar types of MWNT in hundreds of tons a year, a quantity that is greater, but not hugely so, than the current production of Hyperion Catalysis. This is an indication that even these less impressive and exotic nanotubes hold promise of representing a sizable market in the near future.

Nanohorns

These are single-walled carbon cones with structures similar to those of nanotube caps that have been produced by high temperature treatment of fullerene soot. Sumio Iijima's group at NEC has demonstrated that nanohorns have good adsorptive and catalytic properties (i.e. desired substances stick to them and they enhance chemical reactions), and the company is working on using them in a new generation of fuel cells for personal electronics.

This term to refer to hollow and solid carbon fibers with lengths on the order of a few microns and widths varying from some tens of nanometers to around 200 nanometers. These materials have occasionally been referred to as nanotubes. However, they do not have the cylindrical chicken wire structure of SWNTs and MWNTs but instead consist of a mixture of forms of carbon, from layers of graphite stacked at various angles to amorphous carbon. Because of this variable structure they do not exhibit the strength of pure nanotubes but can still be quite strong and possess other useful properties. The US company Applied Sciences Inc. is already producing tons of such material a year and there are several major producers in the Far East.

Production Processes of Carbon Nanotube

Production processes for carbon nanotubes, crudely described, vary from blasting carbon with an electrical arc or a laser to growing them from a vapour, either en masse or on nano particles, sometimes in predetermined positions. These processes vary considerably with respect to the type of nanotube produced, quality, purity and scalability.

Carbon nanotubes are usually created with the aid of a metal catalyst and this ends up as a contaminant with respect to many potential applications, especially in electronics. IBM have very recently, however, grown nanotubes on silicon structures without a metal catalyst. Scalability of production processes is an essential commercial consideration-some of the approaches use equipment that simply cannot be made bigger and the only way to increase production is to make more pieces of equipment, which will not produce the economies of scale required to bring down costs significantly.

Nanotube Applications

Reports of one company producing tons of the material, alongside reports of researchers not being able to get enough to get meaningful results from their research, should no longer be confusing. It would, of course, be useful if commentators got into the habit of making clear the type of material they are talking about. Understanding these differences is essential for understanding the commercial potential of the various applications of nanotubes and related structures that already exist or have been proposed. The variety of these is vast, and the commercialization timelines involved vary from now to ten years from now or more. Some of the potential markets are enormous. The materials markets are already seeing applications for composites based on multi-walled carbon nanotubes and nanofibers.

In many ways this is an old market-that of carbon fibers, which have been around commercially for a couple of decades. The benefits of the new materials in these markets are the same as those of carbon fibers, just better; the main properties to be considered being strength and conductivity.

Carbon fibers are quite large, typically about a tenth of a millimetre in diameter, and blacken the material to which they are added. MWNTs can offer the same improvements in strength to a polymer composite without the blackening and often with a smaller amount of added material. The greater aspect ratio (i.e. length compared to diameter) of the newer materials can make plastics conducting with a smaller filler load, one significant application being electrostatic painting of composites in products such as car parts.

Additionally, the surface of the composite is smoother, which benefits more refined structures such as platens for computer disk drives. When thinking about structural applications such as these, it should be remembered that, in general, as the fibers get smaller so the number of defects decreases, in a progression towards the perfection of the single-walled nanotube.

The inverse progression is seen in terms of ease of manufacturing-the more perfect, and thus more structurally valuable, the material, the harder it is to produce in quantity at a good price. This relationship is not written in stone-there is no reason that near-perfect SWNTs should not be producible cheaply and in large quantities. When this happens, and it might not be too far off, the improvements seen in the strength-to-weight ratios of composite materials could soar, impacting a wide variety of industries from sports equipment to furniture, from the construction industry to kitchenware, and from automobiles to airplanes and spacecraft (the aerospace industry is probably the one that stands to reap the greatest rewards). In fact a carbon nanotube composite has recently been reported that is six times stronger than conventional carbon fiber composites.

This is an appropriate point at which to introduce a note of caution, and an area of research worth keeping an eye on. Just because the perfect nanotube is 100 times stronger than steel at a sixth of the weight doesn't mean you are going to be able to achieve those properties in a bulk material containing them. You may remember that the chicken wire arrangement that makes up the layers in graphite does not stick at all well to other materials, which is why graphite is used in lubricants and pencils.

The same holds true of nanotubes-they are quite insular in nature, preferring not to interact with other materials. To capitalize on their strength in a composite they need to latch on to the surrounding polymer, which they are not inclined to do. One way of making a nanotube interact with something else, such as a surrounding polymer, is to modify it chemically. This is called functionalization and is being explored not just for composite applications but also for a variety of others, such as biosensors. For structural applications, the problem is that functionalization can reduce the valuable qualities of the nanotubes that you are trying to capitalize on. This is an issue that should not be underestimated.

Of course, in theory you don't need to mix the nanotubes with another material. If you want to make super-strong cables the best solution would be to use bundles of sufficiently long nanotubes with no other material added. For this reason, one of the dreams of nanotube production is to be able to spin them, like thread, to indefinite lengths. Such a technology would have applications from textiles to the 'space elevator'.

The space elevator concept, which sounds like something straight out of science fiction involves anchoring one end of a huge cable to the earth and another to an object in space. The taut cable so produced could then support an elevator that would take passengers and cargo into orbit for a fraction of the cost of the rockets used today. Sounds too far out? It has, in fact, been established by NASA as feasible in principle, given a material as strong as SWNTs.

The engineering challenges, though, are awesome, so don't expect that 'top floor' button to be taking you into orbit any time soon. The materials market is a big one, and there are others, which we'll come to, but smaller ones exist too. Nanotubes are already being shipped on the tip of atomic force microscope probes to enhance atomic-resolution imaging. Nanotube-based chemical and biosensors should be on the market soon.

The thermal conductivity of nanotubes shows promise in applications from cooling integrated circuits to aerospace materials. Electron beam lithography, which is a method of producing nanoscale patterns in materials, may become considerably cheaper thanks to the field emission properties of carbon nanotubes. Recent developments show promise of the first significant change in X-ray technology in a century. Entering more speculative territory, nanotubes may one day be used as nanoscale needles that can inject substances into, or sample substances from, individual cells, or they could be used as appendages for miniature machines.

Big markets, apart from materials, in which nanotubes may make an impact, include flat panel displays, lighting, fuel cells and electronics. This last is one of the most talked-about areas but one of the farthest from commercialization, with one exception, this being the promise of huge computer memories (more than a thousand times greater in capacity than what you probably have in your machine now) that could, in theory, put a lot of the $40 billion magnetic disk industry out of business. Companies like to make grand claims, however, and in this area there is not just the technological hurdle to face but the even more daunting economic one, a challenge made harder by a host of competing technologies.

Double-wall Carbon Nanotubes

The study of carbon nanotubes have been divided largely into two categories: the study of multi-wall nanotubes (MWNTs) and the study of single-wall nanotubes (SWNTs). While some experiments show similarities between the two species, others reveal stark differences. For instance, some transport measurements show that MWNTs are diffusive conductors of electric current while SWNTs are ballistic. Arc synthesis methods that produce double-wall boron nitride nanotubes have been known for some time, and recent studies have also demonstrated that controlled synthesis of double-wall carbon nanotubes is also possible. Temperature or electron-beam induced fusing of C_{60} encapsulated inside SWNTs has been used to produce double-wall structures, but in this case the inner 'wall' formed by the C_{60} is not continuous for the entire length of the nanotube. More conventional nanotube synthesis methods have had a disappointingly low yield of carbon DWNTs, and methods that have high yields require specialised apparatus, exotic ceramic precursors, or sulphur-containing precursors. The method is an adaptation of well-established chemical vapour deposition (CVD) methods of producing SWNTs.

The alumina particles have a typical size of 13 nm, and thus produce nm-sized particles of iron salts after evaporation of the solvent. The nanotube synthesis is initiated at approximately 900°C in flowing argon gas. As the alumina/iron salt mixture is heated, the iron salt forms iron oxide, from which the nanotubes grow. To initiate the nanotube growth, the argon is replaced with flowing methane. After 10 min, the gas is switched back to argon and the sample is allowed to cool.

A typical transmission electron microscope (TEM) image of the resulting nanotubes can be seen in Fig. 4. In this image, two DWNTs can be clearly seen, as well as one SWNT. More extensive TEM imaging shows that the nanotubes throughout the sample have outer diameters ranging from 1 to 4 nm, and that the diameters of the nanotubes are uncorrelated to wall numbering (i.e. whether they have one or two walls).

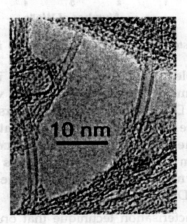

Figure 4. A typical sample from the CVD synthesis of DWNTs.

The distribution of wall numbers in a sample from a typical synthesis run is shown in Fig. 5. From the distribution, it can be seen that two-wall nanotubes dominate the synthesis products. The method also produces a limited number of nanotubes with three or more walls, but more than 90% of the nanotubes present have either one or two walls.

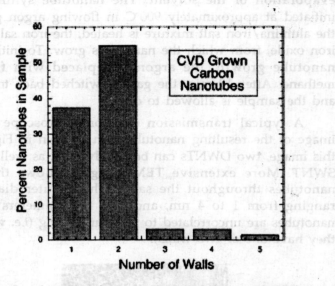

Figure 5. A histogram from counting nanotubes in TEM images.

Several examples of DWNTs are shown in Fig. 6. As is shown, the diameters of the nanotubes can vary greatly. We have observed DWNT with outer diameters as small as 1.3 nm and as large as 5-6 nm. This demonstrates that by outer diameter alone, it is not possible to conclude that a nanotube grown by similar CVD techniques is a SWNT. It is not yet known what synthesis parameters cause the preference for DWNTs.

Any characterisation technique that only examines the external morphology of the nanotubes, such as atomic force microscopy, scanning tunnelling microscopy, or scanning electron microscopy (SEM), does not have the capability to distinguish between single-wall and doublewall nanotubes. In fact, the morphology of the DWNTs more closely resembles that of SWNTs than traditional MWNTs.

Furthermore, the commonly used technique of TEM has the ability to distinguish single-wall structures from doublewall structures only under optimum conditions.

Figure 6. Four double-wall carbon nanotubes (DWCNT) of different diameters.

Fig. 6 shows the same DWNT in two separate TEM images. In the top image, both nanotube walls are clearly resolved with inner tube and outer tube diameters of 1.1 and 1.8 nm, respectively. In addition to providing a bridge between SWNTs and MWNTs, there are many possibilities for future studies on properties that could be unique to DWNTs. For instance, vibrational coupling between nanotubes has been studied in the thermal conductivity and heat capacity of SWNTs bundled together. DWNTs would be ideal for studying the vibrational coupling between two concentric tubes. Such information could be revealed by heat capacity, thermal conductivity, or low frequency Raman spectrometry. Additionally, if the two walls are indeed decoupled, and can slide easily relative to one another: a DWNT presents the smallest possible geometry for realising nanoscale bearings.

There is also substantial interest in the chiral wrapping angle formed by nanotubes, and whether successive walls of MWNTs have chiral angles that are correlated in any way. DWNTs would be ideal for studying these relationships. This type of information could be revealed by either electron diffraction or high-resolution TEM. Specifically, it would be interesting to study whether or not the two walls of a DWNT always form a commensurate structure, or whether incommensurate structures are possible. This would have a significant impact on possible nanobearing applications. The chirality relationships in DWNT's could also have relevance to various growth models that have been proposed for MWNTs.

5

Novel Nanomaterials

Nanotechnology has created the most excitement and publicity. In a mature nanotech world, macro structures would simply be grown fro m their smallest constituent components: an 'anything box' would take a molecular seed containing instructions for building a product and use tiny nanobots or molecular machines to build it atom by atom. Indeed, as Forrest points out, 'the development of [bottom-up] technology does not depend upon on discovering new scientific principles.

The advances required a re-engineering.' In short, fully-fledged bottom-up nanotechnology promises nothing less than complete control over the physical structure of matter—the same kind of control over the molecular and structural make-up of physical objects that a word processor provides over the form and content of text. At present it is clear that this bottom-up 'dream' is far from being realised. As Saxl notes: 'Top-down and bottom-up can be a measure of the level of advancement of nanotechnology, and nanotechnology, as applied today, is still mainly in the top-down stage.' This state of relative infancy is often compared in the literature to the information technology (IT) sector in the 1960s, or biotechnology in the 1980s. So, with the science fiction aspects of the debate rapidly receding, industry has now necessarily adopted much more realistic expectations.

In fact, current industry jargon would probably describe nanotechnology as 'coming on stream'. For, although the underlying technologies and their applications are still at an early stage of development, there are applications emerging into the market that are likely to be making a significant impact on the industrial scene by 2006.

The best evidence of this move into commercialisation concerns the recent emergence of three alliances whose sole purpose is to translate this underlying research into economically viable products: the US NanoBusiness Alliance, the Europe Nanobusiness Association, and the Asia-Pacific Nanotechnology Forum. In addition to this, laboratories around the world are working on new approaches and on new ways to scale up nanotechnology to industrial levels. For example, the first factories to manufacture carbon nanotubes and fullerenes are under construction in Japan. In spite of these developments, there has been criticism recently over the amount of hype and, consequently, funding that research into nanoscience and nanotechnology has received.

The much-heralded US National Nanotechnology Initiative (NNI) has been criticised for using 'nano' as a convenient tag to attract funding for a whole range of new science and technologies. This reinvention is one way of attracting more money because politicians like to feel they are putting money into something new and exciting. For these reasons, the nanotechnology sector is far broader than you would usually expect to see and the resulting lack of a clear definition is hampering meaningful discussion of its potential costs or benefits.

Research and Development

Research encompassing many areas of work that have traditionally been referred to as chemistry or biology. Thus, the first major characteristic of activity grouped under this section is that contemporary R&D cuts across a wide range of industrial sectors. In some cases, major markets are fairly well defined. The food industry serves as a good example here, where there are significant drivers at work. To illustrate, 'smart' wrappings for the food industry (that indicate freshness or otherwise) are close to the market. By 2006, beer packaging is anticipated by industry to use the highest weight of nano-strengthened material, at 3 million lbs., followed by meats and carbonated soft drinks. By 2011, meanwhile, the total figure might reach almost 100 million lbs.

In other cases, important applications are identified but the eventual market impacts are more difficult to predict. For example, nanotechnology is anticipated to yield significant advances in catalyst technology. If these potential applications are realised then the impact on society will be dramatic as catalysts, arguably the most important technology in our modern society, enable the production of a wide range of materials and fuels. A second characteristic of current work in this area is that the kinds of materials and processes being developed are necessarily 'technology pushed': urged on by the potential impacts of nanotechnology, the R&D community is achieving rapid advances in basic science and technology.

This level of scientific interest is gauged by Compano and Hullman who examine the world- wide number of publications in nanotechnology in the Science Citation Index (SCI) database. They conclude that for the period between 1989 and 1998 the average annual growth rate in the number of publications is an 'impressive' 27%. This rise in interest is not confined to a small number of central repositories however. Instead, research is spread across more than 30 countries that have developed nanotechnology activities and plans.

In this way, Compano and Hullman also examine the distribution of this interest. Based upon their findings, the most active is the US, with roughly one-quarter of all publications, followed by Japan, China, France, the UK and Russia. These countries alone account for 70% of the world's scientific papers on nanotechnology. In particular, for China and Russia the shares are outstanding in comparison with their general presence in the SCI database and show the significance of nanoscience in their research systems.

The third major characteristic of activity grouped under this section concerns that fact that nanotechnology is primarily about making things. For this reason, most of the existing focus of R&D centres on 'nanomaterials': novel materials whose molecular structure has been engineered at the nanometre scale. Indeed, Saxl states that: 'material science and technology is fundamental to a majority of the applications of nanotechnology.' Thus, many of the materials that follow involve either bulk production of conventional compounds that are much smaller (and hence exhibit different properties) or new nanomaterials, such as fullerenes and nanotubes. The markets range of nanomaterials are considerable. Indeed, it has been estimated that, aided by nanotechnology, novel materials and processes can be expected to have a market impact of over US$340 billion within a decade.

Nanotubes

Nanotubes provide a good example of how basic R&D can take off into full-scale market application in one specific area. Described as 'the most important material in nanotechnology today', nanotubes are a new material with remarkable tensile strength. Indeed, taking current technical barriers into account, nanotube-based material is anticipated to become 50-100 times stronger than steel at one-sixth of the weight.

This development would dwarf the improvements that carbon fibres brought to composites. Harry Kroto, who was awarded the Nobel Prize for the discovery of C_{60}

Buckminsterfullerene, states that such advances will take 'a long, long time' to achieve, the first applications of nanotubes being in composite development. However, if such technologies do eventually arrive, the results will be awesome: they will 'be equivalent to James Watt's invention of the condenser', a development that kick-started the industrial revolution. The concept of the space elevator serves as a good illustration of the kind of visionary thinking that recent nanotube development has inspired.

The idea of a 'lift to the stars' is not itself particularly new: a Russian engineer, Yuri Artutanov, penned the idea of an elevator—perhaps powered by a laser that could quietly transport payloads and people to a space platform— as early as 1960. However, such ideas have always been hampered by the lack of material strength necessary to make the cable attachment.

The nanotube may be the key to overcoming this longstanding obstacle, making the space elevator a reality in just 15 years time. This development, though, will rely on the successful incorporation of nanotubes into fibres or ribbons and successfully avoiding various atmospheric dangers, such as lightning strikes, micrometeors, and human-made space debris. The market impetus behind such developments, then, is clear: the conventional space industry is anticipated as the first major customer, followed by aircraft manufacturers. However, as production costs drop, nanotubes are expected to find widespread application in such large industries as automobiles and construction.

In fact, it is possible to conceive of a market in any area of industry that will benefit from lighter and stronger materials. It is expectations such as these that are currently fuelling the race to develop techniques of nanotube massproduction in economic quantities. For example, Japan's Mitsui and Co. will start building a facility in April 2003 with an annual production capacity of 120 tons of carbon nanotubes. The company plans to market the product to automakers, resin makers and battery makers. In fact, the industry has grown so quickly that Holister believes that the number of nanotube suppliers already in existence are not likely to be supported by available applications in the years to come. Fried also supports this contention, stating that the 'carbon nanotube field is already over-saturated'.

Fabrication Tools

It is a simple statement of fact that in order to make things you must first have the fabrication tools available. Therefore, many of the nanomaterials covered above are co-evolving with a number of enabling technologies and techniques.

These tools provide the instrumentation needed to examine and characterise devices and effects during the R&D phase, the manufacturing techniques that will allow the large—scale economic production of nanotechnology products, and the necessary support for quality control. Because of the essential nature of this category, its influence is far greater than is reflected in the size of the economic sectors producing these products. For this reason, the tools and techniques highlighted below have a strong commercial future and the greatest number of established companies. However, in the near future, this area will mainly feature extensions of conventional instrumentation and top-down manufacturing. More futuristic molecular scale assembly remains distant.

Top-down manufacture

Scanning Probe Microscope: This is the general term for a range of instruments with specific functions. Fundamentally, a nanoscopic probe is maintained at a constant height over the bed of atoms. This probe can be positioned so close to individual atoms that the electrons of the probe-tip and atom begin to interact.

These interactions can be strong enough to 'lift' the atom and move it to another place. Optical Techniques. These techniques can be used to detect movement - obviously important in hi-tech precision engineering. Optical techniques are, in theory, restricted in resolution to half the wavelength of light being used, which keeps them out of the lower nanoscale, but various approaches are now overcoming this limitation.

Lithographics: Lithography is the means by which patterns are delineated on silicon chips and micro-electrical-mechanical systems (MEMS). Most significantly, optical lithography is the dominant exposure tool in use today in the semiconductor industry's Complementary Metal Oxide Semiconductor (CMOS) process

Bottom-up manufacture

The tools here support rather more futuristic approaches to large-scale production and nanofabrication based on bottom-up approaches, such as nanomachine production lines. This approach is equivalent to building a car engine up from individual components, rather than the less intuitive method of machining a system down from large blocks of material. Indeed, although such techniques are still in their infancy, the DTI report a recent movement away from top-down techniques towards self-assembly within the international research community. Scientists and engineers are becoming increasingly able to understand, intervene and rearrange the atomic and molecular structure of matter, and control its form in order to achieve specific aims.

Self-assembly and self-organisation. Selfassembly refers to the tendency of some materials to organise themselves into ordered arrays. This technique potentially offers huge economies, and is considered to have great potential in nanoelectronics. In particular, the study of the self-assembly nature of molecules is proving to be the foundation of rapid growth in applications in science and technology. For example, Saxl reports that the Stranski-Krastonov methods for growing self-assembly quantum dots has rendered the lithographic approach to semiconductor quantum dot fabrication virtually obsolete.

In addition, self-assembly is leading to the fabrication of new materials and devices. The former area of materials consists of new types of nanocomposites or organic/inorganic hybrid structures that are created by depositing or attaching organic molecules to ultra-small particles or ultra-thin manmade layered structures. Similarly, the latter area of devices range from the production of new chemical and gas sensors, optical sensors, solar panels and other energy conversion devices, to bioimplants and in vivo monitoring. The basis of these technologies is an organic film (the responsive layer) which can be deposited on a hard, active electronic chip substrate. The solid-state chip receives signals from the organic over-layer as it reacts to changes in its environment, and processes them.

Molecular Modelling Software

Molecular modelling software is another fabrication technique of wide-ranging applicability as it permits the efficient analysis of large molecular structures and substrates. Hence, it is much used by molecular nanotechnologists, where computers can simulate the behaviour of matter at the atomic and molecular level. In addition, computer modelling is anticipated to prove essential in understanding and predicting the behaviour of nanoscale structures because they operate at what is sometimes referred to as the mesoscale, an area where both classical and quantum physics influence behaviour.

Nanometrology

Fundamental to commercial nanotechnology is repeatability, and fundamental to repeatability is measurement. Nanometrology, then, allows the perfection of the texture at the nanometre and subnanometre level to be examined and controlled. This is essential if highly specialised applications of nanotechnology are to operate correctly, for example X-ray optical components and mirrors used in laser technologies.

The main reason for government interest in nanotechnology is strategic: to achieve an advantageous position so that when nanotech applications begin to have a significant effect in the world economy, countries are able to exploit these new opportunities to the full.

Levels of public investment in nanotechnology are reminiscent of a growing strategic interest: this is an area that attracts both large and small countries. Global R&D spending is currently around US$4 billion, with public investment increasing rapidly. Table 2 summarises these rises. The US is widely considered to be the worldleader in nanoscale science research. Certainly, in terms of leading centres for nanotechnology research, the USA dominates, with eight institutions making the DTI top list of 13. These centres are University of Santa Barbara, Cornell University, University of California at Los Angeles, Stanford University, IBM Research Laboratories, Northwestern University, Harvard University and the Massachusetts Institute of Technology (MIT).

In total, more than 30 universities have announced plans for nanotech research centres since 1997. Further, the US is widely regarded as the benchmark against which nanotechnology funding should be compared. From 1985-1997 the total support for projects related to nanotechnology was estimated at US$452 million, coming in roughly equal parts from the NSF, various industrial sponsorship, and other government funding. Then in 2000, the much-heralded NNI was launched - a multiagency programme designed to provide a big funding boost for nanotechnology.

There are currently 10 US government partners in the NNI3. Indeed, the NSF has designated 'nanoscale science and engineering' as one of its six priority areas, while the DoD has dedicated its funding to elaborating a 'conceptual template for achieving new levels of war-fighting effectiveness'. All European Union (EU) member states, except Luxembourg where no universities are located, have research programmes.

For some countries, such as Germ any, Ireland or Sweden, where nanotechnology is considered of strategic importance, nanotechnology programmes have been established for several years. On the other hand, many countries have no specifically focused nanotechnology initiatives, but this research is covered within more general R&D programmes. The European Commission (EC) funds nanoscience through its so-called Framework Programme (FP). The aim of the FP6 is to produce breakthrough technologies that directly benefit the EU, either economically or socially. Under this, ε1.3 billion are earmarked for 'nanotechnologies and nanosciences, knowledge-based multifunctional materials and new production processes and devices' in the 2002-2006 FP out of a total budget of ε11.3 billion.

This thematic priority is only partly dedicated to nanoscience, while other thematic priorities also have a nanotechnology component. At first glance this may seem a small figure compared to the 2003 NNI budget of US$710 million. However, it does not take into account the substantial contributions made by individual member states. The UK serves as a good example of this, where public spending on nanotechnology R&D was around £30 million in 2001, 70-80% of it from the Engineering and

Physical Sciences Research Council (EPSRC). However, this is set to rise quite rapidly in 2002-2003 as the new interdisciplinary research collaborations and university technology centres start to spread.

Applications of Nanotechnology

The applications of nanotechnology are extremely diverse, mainly because the field is interdisciplinary. In addition, the effect that nanotechnology will have during the next decade is difficult to estimate because of potentially new and unanticipated applications. For example, if simply reducing the microstructure in existing materials can make a big market impact, then this may, in turn, lead to a whole new set of applications. However, it seems reasonable to assume that during the next two to three years most activity in nanotechnology will still be in the area of research, rather than completed projects or products. Holister estimates that there are currently 455 public and private companies, 95 investors, and 271 academic institutions and government entities that are involved in the near-term applications of nanotechnology world-wide.

The ability of such institutions to transfer research results into industrial applications can be indicated by the number of filed patents. Compano and Hullman provide an analysis of this, using the number of nanopatents filed at the European Patent Office (EPO) in Munich. Over the whole 1981-1998 period, the number of nanopatents rises from 28-180 patents, with an average growth rate in the 1990s amounting to 7%. One important characteristic of activity grouped within this section is that much of the work in near-term applications of nanotechnologies is 'market-pulled': in each case, a particular and potentially profitable use within industry and/or the consumer market has been identified. However, as with the difficulty in predicting the future applications of nanotechnology, many market analysts believe that it is too soon to produce reliable figures for the global market - it is simply too early to say where and when markets and applications will come. In spite of these difficulties, some forecasts exist that do hint at the kind of growth we might expect. Most strikingly, the NSF predicts that the total market for nanotech products and services will reach US$1 trillion by 2015.

The accuracy of this claim is difficult to assess, given the doubts expressed above. Compano and Hullman approach the problem through the comparison of publication (representing basic science or R&D) and patent (representing technology applications) nanotechnology data with Grupp's theory of Stylised Technological Development. As a result, they conclude that the peak of scientific activity is still to come, possibly in three to five years from now, and large-scale exploitation of nanotechnological results might arise ten years from now. Considering the above comments about nanotechnological development and marketpull, it is instructive to examine which areas of industry will be affected first. Mihail Roco, the NSF senior advisor for nanotechnology, believes that 'early payoffs will come in computing and pharmaceuticals', whereas Holister points out that medicine is a huge market, thereby implying that revenue for nanotechnology in this area could be substantial.

On the other hand, the NSF believe that, due to the high initial costs involved, 'nanotechnology-based goods and services will probably be introduced earlier in those markets where performance characteristics are especially important and price is a secondary consideration'. Examples of these are medical applications and space exploration. The experience gained will then reduce technical and production uncertainties and prepare these technologies for deployment into the market place.

A good indication of the areas of current and near-future commercial nanotech activity is the type of patents made. Compano and Hullman state that one-quarter of all patents filed are focused on instrumentation. This supports the view that nanotechnology is at the beginning of the development phase of an enabling technology where the first focus is to develop suitable tools and fabrication techniques.

The most important industrial sectors are informatics (information science), and pharmaceuticals and chemicals. For the first sector, 'massive storage devices, flat panel displays, or electronic paper are prominent IT patenting areas. In addition to this, extended semiconductor approaches and alternative nanoscale information processing, transmission or storage devices are dominant.' In the case of chemistry and pharmaceuticals, a large number of patents are directed towards 'finding new approaches for drug delivery, medical diagnosis, and cancer treatments which are supposed to have huge future markets. Nanotechnology patenting for other sectors (e.g. aerospace, construction industries and food processing) show yearly increasing values, but their absolute numbers are relatively small.'

Information science

Informatics, or information science, can be thought of as consisting of three interrelated areas: electronics, magnetics and optics. In fact, the current market for miniaturised systems is estimated at US\$40 billion and the market for IT peripherals to be more than US\$20 billion, although semiconductor products have a dominant role and their turnover grows at a higher rate than the overall electronics market. The field is dominated by the US and Japan. In fact, apart from a few niche markets where Western European companies are able to compete, recent technological breakthroughs have been largely due to major manufacturers in these countries. Japan has a particularly strong commercial basis in this area, although Japanese R&D tends to be organised through lines determined by the government: the METI funds much of the work.

In the US too, government is very involved in applied research. Here, the activities of military funding agencies are of note - such institutions tend to be generous in their company funding in this field, even when there is a clear commercial benefit for the companies involved. In general, it is much harder to predict the commercially successful technologies in the world of electronics than in the world of materials. However, if one considers that the major driving force in nanoscience for the last decade has been microelectronics, then it makes sense that nanotechnology will play an important role in the future of this industry.

The ETC Group provide a notable statistic here, stating that by 2012 the entire market will be dependent on nanotech. For, although there are few nanotechnology products in the market place at present, future growth is expected to be strong, with a predicted composite annual growth rate of 30-40%, with emerging markets around 70%. A number of recent forecasts, although varying greatly, reflect this market confidence.

Law of Moore

The microelectronics industry had looked ahead and seen serious challenges for its basic CMOS process. CMOS technology has been refined for over 20 years, driving the 'line width'-the width of the smallest feature in an integrated circuit (IC)-from 10 mm down to 0.25 µm. This is the force behind Moore's law, which predicts that the processing power of ICs will double every 18 months. Semiconductor industry associations assume that they will be close to introducing 100 nm ground-rule technology by 2004. The significance of this lies in the fact that 100 nm is widely viewed as a kind of 'turning point', where many radically new technologies will have to be developed. To begin with, optical lithography will become obsolete somewhere around 100 nm. As a result, 'next generation lithography' options are currently being investigated.

Excluding the printing process, each fabrication technique essentially works on the same principle where a reactive siliconbased agent is exposed to increasingly focused electromagnetic radiation: optical to X-rays representing a successive reduction in photon wavelength; E-beam and ion beam projection technologies using focused electron and ion beams respectively.

All of these techniques are currently under active evaluation-the aim is to have the appropriate equipment for the corresponding time-frame. To date, X-ray and ion bean projection have received the greatest research investment. Printing technologies, however, are the ultimate goal, where sheets of circuits can be rolled off the production line like a printing press. Moore's law cannot continue indefinitely. In the years following 2015, additional difficulties are likely to be encountered, some of which may pose serious challenges to traditional semiconductor manufacturing techniques.

In particular, limits to the degree that interconnections or wires between transistors may be scaled could in turn limit the effective computation speed of devices because of the properties and compatibility of particular materials, despite incremental present-day advances in these areas. Thermal dissipation in chips with extremely high device-densities will also pose a serious challenge. This issue is not so much a fundamental limitation as it is an economic consideration, in that heat dissipation mechanisms and cooling technology may be required that add to the total system cost, thereby adversely affecting the marginal cost per computational function for these devices.

Eventually, however, CMOS technology may hit a more crucial barrier, the quantum world, where the laws of physics operate in a very different paradigm to that experienced in everyday life. For example, futuristic circuits operating on a quantum scale would have to take Heisenberg's Uncertainty Principle into account. Overcoming this barrier is a different matter altogether, where the problems are no longer merely technological, and industry has already begun to investigate the problem in a number of ways. Three of the most commonly cited approaches—molecular nanoelectronics and quantum information processing (QIP)-are expanded upon below. In addition, computational self-assembly is acknowledged as a potentially key fabrication technique of the future.

Organic molecules have been shown to have the necessary properties to be used in electronics. Devices made of molecular components would be much smaller than those made by existing silicon technologies and ultimately offer the smallest electronics theoretically possible without moving into the realm of subatomic particles. Molecular electronic devices could operate as logic switches through chemical means, using synthesised organic compounds. These devices can be assembled chemically in large numbers and organised to form a computer. The main advantage of this approach is significantly lower power consumption by individual devices.

Several approaches for such devices have been devised, and experiments have shown evidence of switching behaviour for individual devices. For example, in 'DNA computing', the similarities between mathematical operations and biological reactions are used to perform calculations. The key idea is to find the parallelism between DNA-the basic genetic information-and well-known digital computers. This is because a string of DNA can be used to solve combination problems if it can be put together in the right sequence. One issue is that molecular memories must be able to maintain their state, just as in a digital electronic computer. Also, given that the manufacturing and assembly process for these devices will lead to device defects, a defect-tolerant computer architecture needs to be developed. Fabricating reliable interconnections between devices using carbon nanotubes is an additional challenge.

A significant amount of work is ongoing in each of these areas. Even though experimental progress to date in this area has been substantial, it seems unlikely that molecular computers could be developed within the next 15 years that would be relatively attractive compared with conventional electronic computers.

QIP: This crosses the disciplines of quantum physics, computer science, information theory and engineering with the aim of harnessing the fundamental laws of quantum physics to 'dramatically improve the acquisition, transmission and processing of information'. QIP represents computing at the smallest possible scale, in which one atom is equivalent to one byte of information. Other aspects of quantum computing also considered attractive relate to their massive parallelism in computation.

These concepts are qualitatively different from those employed in traditional computers and will hence require new computer architectures. A preliminary survey of work in this area by Anton et al., indicates that quantum switches are unlikely to overcome major technical obstacles, such as 'error correction, de-coherence and signal input/output' within the next 15 years. If this proves to be the case, QIP-based computing, as with molecular nanoelectronics, does not appear to be competitive with traditional digital electronic computers for some time. Computational self-assembly. A major barrier to the introduction of nanoelectronics is that there are no established mass production techniques for creating devices on a commercial basis.

The relatively straightforward architecture of molecular memory means that self-assembly techniques in this area may bear fruit in a few years. Tackling processors is another matter, however, because of the greater complexity involved-their applicability remains limited until total control over the emerging structures in terms of wiring and their interconnections can be obtained. These are formidable obstacles. Self-assembly, therefore, will likely be combined initially with some more traditional top-down approaches. For example, many believe that inducing molecular components to selfassemble on a patterned substrate in some sort of hybrid system will represent the first commercialisation of nanoelectronics.

New technology in energy sector

The global energy sector is likely to be particularly affected by coming advances in nanotechnology. To illustrate, significant changes in lighting technologies are expected in the next 10-15 years.

Semiconductors used in the preparation of light-emitting diodes can increasingly be sculpted on nanoscale dimensions. Projections indicate that such nanotechnology-based advances have the potential to reduce world-wide consumption of energy by more than 10%. Most current photovoltaic (PV) production is based upon crystalline and amorphous silicon technologies. Nanotechnology is anticipated to play an important part in this future.

Although total PV power output remains relatively low, the industry is growing rapidly-the production of PV modules expanded by 40% in 1997. This increase is largely due to the building and construction industry, the largest and fastest growing sector at present. In addition, developing countries represent a potentially vast market. In spite of these developments, however, nanotechnology, as a new and radical technology, still faces an uncertain future in this area as a number of alternative technologies are also competing for attention (e.g. inorganic silicon).

Nanoscale informatics in defence

Nanoscale informatics, pharmaceuticals and medicine remain the most high-profile areas of near-term market application. However, Gsponer contends that the most significant near-term applications of nanotechnology will be in the military domain. This is because micromechanical and MEMS engineering is historically connected to nuclear weapons laboratories: it was within this domain that the field of nanotechnology was born a few decades ago.

Today, it is not difficult to understand why nanotechnology might appeal to military planners. Through technologies such as steam navigation, repeating firearms, and high explosives, Western powers have enjoyed virtually unchallenged military supremacy throughout the 19th Century. It is not absurd, then, to imagine that nanotechnology could play a similar role in the 21st Century. Indeed, new technologies, notably IT, are playing an increasingly important part in modern warfare-as reflected by recent investments in the US DoD.

Trends such as these have led leading strategic commentators, such as David Jeremiah, to conclude that military applications of nanotechnology have an even greater potential than nuclear weapons to radically change the balance of global power in the future. Fundamentally, this potential lies in a greater range of military options when deciding how to respond to aggression. In peacetime or crisis, nanocomputers may allow more capable surveillance of potential aggressors.

The flood of data from world-wide sensors could be culled more efficiently to look for truly threatening activities. In low-intensity warfare, intelligent sensors and barrier systems could isolate or channel guerrilla movements depending on the local terrain. In conventional theatre war, nanotechnology may lead to small, cheap, highly lethal antitank weapons. Such weapons could allow relatively small numbers of infantry to defeat assaults by large armoured forces.

At nuclear conflict levels, accurate nanocomputer guidance and low nanomachine production costs would accelerate current trends in the proliferation of 'smart' munitions. Rather than requiring nuclear weapons to attack massive conventional forces or distant, hard targets, nanotechnology enhancements to cruise missiles and ballistic missiles could allow them to destroy their targets with conventional explosives. In addition, such nanotechnologies might be 'cleaner' and 'safer' and less likely to cause collateral damage than the technologies they replace, making them especially appealing to military planners.

MEMS have many potential uses in the battlefield, largely due to their built-in mechanical functions that allow them to act as sensors and actuators. Actuators in particular extend the functionality of sensors by allowing them to respond to the environment with the usage of force. Applications of MEMS in military systems include ammunition, petroleum, food, as well as enabling a host of other smarter, more efficient logistics operations. The infantry soldier too is anticipated to receive a nanotech-based 'makeover': a new Institute for Soldier Nanotechnology (ISN) has been created at MIT, with a US Army grant of US$50 million over five years. The goal of this research centre is to greatly enhance the protection and survival of the infantry soldier using nanoscience. For example, US army planners are hoping to lighten the load that soldiers carry into battle (currently around 64 kg) by redesigning the equipment from the atomic scale up.

Technologies in transnational companies

Transnational companies often carry out their own nanotech-related R&D. This is because they understand that nanotechnology is likely to disrupt their current products and processes, and therefore recognise the need to understand and control the pace of such implications. In this way, some of the world's largest companies, including IBM, Motorola, Hewlett Packard, Lucent, Hitachi, Mitsubishi, NEC, Corning, Dow Chemical and 3M have launched significant nanotech initiatives through their own venture capital funds or as a direct result of their own R&D.

In the US and Switzerland for example, IBM is providing some US$100 million nanotechrelated funding for its hi-tech research laboratories. In Japan too, many of the nation's largest players have now entered the nanotech field, including Fuji, Hewlett-Packard Japan, Hitachi, Mitsubishi, NEC and Sony. For example, Toray Industries, a global maker of synthetic fibre, textiles and chemicals, is establishing a US$40 million centre specialising in nanotechnology and biotechnology near Tokyo.

The building is expected to be finished by March 2003. At present there are about 100 business start - ups - new business ventures in their earliest stages of development - in operation today, about half of which are located in the US. Such companies rely on their understanding of where new opportunities and markets may lie and thus play an important role in commercialising research. This increase in activity amongst start-ups is mirrored by the investment community, who, according to Abid Khan, have decided that nanotechnology is the 'next big thing' -the new computing or biotechnology. Indeed, some large investment groups now have specialists who follow developments in the subject.

Although such activity tends to produce little in the way of a coherent picture, business investment in nanotechnology start-ups is on the rise. There were over 20 nanotechnology investments in the first half of 2002 in the US and Europe, and more than US$100 million invested in the US in the first half of 2002. According to Thibodeau, this level of funding is projected to increase to US$1 billion by 2003. Nanotechnology advocates have been criticised within recent years for hyping the potential impact that nanoscale science and technology will have upon the economy and society.

6

Nanostructured Materials

Biological systems have built up inorganic-organic nanocomposite structures to improve the mechanical properties or to improve the optical, magnetic and chemical sensing in living species. As an example, nacre (mother-of-pearl) from the mollusc shell is a biologically formed lamellar ceramic, which exhibits structural robustness despite the brittle nature of its constituents.

The systems have evolved and been optimised by evolution over millions of years into sophisticated and complex structures. In natural systems the bottom-up approach starting from molecules and involving self organisation concepts has been highly successful in building larger structural and functional components.

Functional systems are characterised by complex sensing, self repair, information transmission and storage and other functions all based on molecular building blocks. Examples of these complex structures for structural purposes are teeth, such as shark teeth, which consist of a composite of biomineralised fluorapatite and organic compounds. Another example for a biological nanostructure is opal which exhibits unique optical properties.

The self cleaning effects of the surfaces of the lotus flower have been attributed to the combined micro- and nanostructure which in combination with hydrophobic groups give the surface a water and dirt repellent behaviour. In the past few years, numerous companies have realised products resembling the surface morphology and chemistry of the lotus flower such as paint, glass surface and ceramic tiles with dirt repellent properties. The realisation that nature can provide the model for improved engineering has created a research field called bio-mimicking or bio-inspired materials science. It has been possible to process these ceramic-organic nanocomposite structures which provide new technological opportunities and potential for applications.

The biomimetic growth of synthetic fluorapatite in the laboratory and promising new technical applications of these nanomaterials are envisioned. Other man-made nanostructures were manufactured for their attractive optical properties, such as the colloidal gold particles in glass as seen in medieval church windows. While plentiful man made materials with nanostructures have been in use for a long time (partially without knowing it) a change of the scientific and technological approach can be identified over the past two decades.

This change can be related to a few key ideas and discoveries: the idea of assembling nanostructures from atomic, molecular or nanometer sized building blocks, the discovery of new forms of carbon, i.e., fullerenes and carbon nanotubes, and the development of scanning probe microscopy, such as scanning tunneling microscopy (STM) and atomic force microscopy (AFM). With the visionary goals many researchers worldwide have worked intensively on the development of novel or improved synthesis methods, new and better characterisation techniques and the measurement and the design of the properties of nanostructured materials.

In this paper some aspects of the immensely wide field will be described. However, as the field of nanostructured materials is very broad including all classes of materials as well as composites it is not possible and not attempted to consider all developments and all research groups and industries.

Synthesis Method

The microstructure and properties of nanostructured materials depend in an extreme manner on the synthesis method as well as on the processing route. Therefore, it is of utmost importance to select the most appropriate technique for preparation of nanomaterials with desired properties and property combinations. Synthesis techniques can be divided into bottom-up and top-down approaches.

The top-down approach starts with materials with conventional crystalline microstructures, typically metals and alloys, and defects such as dislocations and point defects are introduced by severe plastic deformation such as in equal channel pressing. The recrystallisation of the material leads to finer and finer grain sizes and under certain processing conditions to nanostructured materials. The advantage of these approaches is the fact that bulk nanostructured materials with theoretical density can be prepared.

An alternative to obtain theoretical dense materials is the pulsed electrodeposition method developed by Erb and El-Sherik which yields nanocrystalline strips, however, only with thicknesses of several hundred microns. The bottom-up approach includes many different techniques which are based on liquid or gas phase processes. Classically, wet chemical processes such as precipitation and sol-gel have been employed to obtain nanoparticles, however, with the disadvantage of severe agglomeration.

In the gas phase metallic and ceramic nanoparticles have been synthesised by using Inert Gas Condensation, Flame Pyrolysis and chemical vapour based processes. The major microstructural features in preparing nanoparticles for subsequent use are: nanometer sized primary particles with narrow size distributions, minimum amount of agglomeration, good crystallinity, etc. Two techniques, chemical vapour synthesis (CVS) in the gas phase and electrodeposition under oxidising conditions (EDOC) in the liquid phase, together with the resulting microstructures will be presented in more detail and the advantages and disadvantages be discussed.

CVS is based on chemical vapour deposition (CVD) for the synthesis of thin films and coatings by the decomposition of metalorganic precursors. Whether thin films are deposited by heterogeneous „nucleation or nanoparticles are formed in the gas phase by homogeneous nucleation is determined by the residence time of the precursor in the hot zone of the reactor. The most important parameters determining the growth regime and the particle size are the total pressure, the precursor partial pressure and the temperature of the reaction zone.

When two precursors are used, the precursor delivery can be modified in the following way:

(1) two precursors are introduced simultaneously into the reaction zone yielding doped nanoparticles (i.e. alumina doped zirconia);

(2) two precursors are introduced into two concentric reaction tubes, reacted to form nanoparticles and then mixed in the gas phase to yield a nanocomposite structure (i.e., alumina mixed with zirconia) and

(3) in the first reaction zone the first precursor is decomposed to form nanoparticles by homogeneous nucleation which are subsequently coated in a second reaction zone by introducing the second precursor under conditions which favour CVD deposition (i.e., alumina surface coated zirconia).

Figure 2 shows a high resolution electron image of polymer coated titania nanoparticles where the crystalline titania

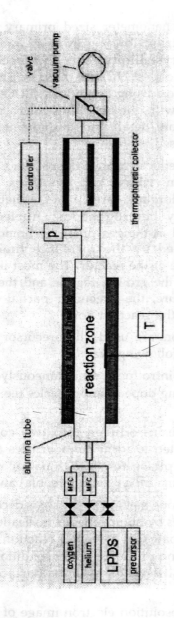

Figure 1. Schematic diagram of the major components of a CVS hot wall reactor: precursor source (liquid precursor delivery system, LPDS), hot wall reaction zone, thermophoretic particle collector, pumping system, and temperature control.

core can be clearly distinguished from the amorphous organic shell on several grains. The modification of the surfaces of nanoparticles allows the improvement of dispersibility in various aqueous and organic solvents which is important for many ceramic processing steps (dip- or spin-coating, slurries for ceramic processing, etc.) and for technical applications of dispersions. Additionally, the inorganic core/polymer shell structure allows the preparation of polymer nanocomposites with excellent separation between the inorganic nanoparticles.

5 nm

Figure 2. High resolution TEM of titania nanoparticles (crystalline core) coated with an amorphous polymeric shell

A further variation by exact control of all synthesis parameters allows the growth of thick nanocrystalline coatings on dense and porous substrates. Depending on the substrate temperature the porosity of the coating can be changed over a wide range up to theoretical density. This intermediate stage, called CVD/CVS, has been successfully used to deposit a nanocrystalline coating of yttrium stabilised zirconia on porous anode substrates for high temperature solid oxide fuel cell applications.

The molecular dynamics (MD) simulation technique to obtain details of the processes during particle formation, agglomeration, and sintering. As the nanoparticles contain only a limited number of atoms, it is possible to study diffusion and rearrangement processes leading to aggregation and particle growth. Atomistic simulations are extremely useful in describing the initial stages of sintering and equilibrium particle morphologies which determine the final structure and properties of nanoparticles prepared in the gas phase.

Figure 3. High resolution SEM of a nanocrystalline coating of yttrium stabilised zirconia on a porous anode substrate

A scaling law was established which allows the comparison to experimental conditions. MD-simulations have been employed for many other processes in nanocrystalline materials such as the calculation of the elastic properties of nanocrystalline nickel and the plastic and superplastic deformation of nanocrystalline metals and the atomistic structure and energies of grain boundaries in nanocrystalline metals.

The EDOC process was developed to synthesise nanocrystalline oxides with improved properties as compared to oxides obtained by precipitation and sol-gel routes. In particular, it was attempted to improve the control on size and size distribution, the dispersibility and the possibility to modify the surfaces of the nanocrystalline powders. In the EDOC process an anode, i.e., metallic Zn, is dissolved in an organic electrolyte with an organic conducting salt by applying a voltage. The Zn^{2+}-ions migrate to an inert cathode, are discharged and subsequently oxidised by means of bubbling air through the electrolyte, thus forming ZnO-nanoparticles. The conducting salt has the additional role to prevent continued growth of the nanoparticles and their agglomeration.

After filtration, the nanoparticles can be further modified or functionalised by exchanging the organic shell by other molecules to adapt the surface chemistry to other chemical environments. Other metal oxides have been prepared by EDOC, such as SnO_2, TiO_2, and ZrO_2 as well as doped oxides. Compared to other wet chemical processes, the EDOC nanopowders exhibit superior dispersibility in solvents.

In many processes, the microstructure, the morphology, the size and size distribution, the agglomeration and the elemental distribution on the scale of the nanoparticles can be controlled. In addition, it is possible to control the surface chemistry and thus to control the reactivity of the nanomaterials with the environment. The availability of versatile synthesis techniques is the prerequisite for materials design on the nanometer scale.

Characterisation of Nanostructures Materials

The characterisation of nanostructured materials in the form of thin films, nanoparticles and bulk structures demands special techniques which allow for the structural and chemical analysis with a sufficient lateral resolution. Consequently, special characterisation techniques are required besides the standard techniques available to materials science.

The extremely high surface and interface areas have to be considered. Experimental difficulties such as oxidation/ reaction at surfaces, the disordered structure at the grain boundaries and other internal interfaces and substantial porosity can be present in these materials. The specific surface area of nanopowders with average grain sizes below 10 nm can rise to several hundred m^2/g. That is, two to three grams of nanopowders which fit into a small volume of a few cm^3 can have the same surface area as an entire football field.

Therefore, nanocrystalline powders are considered to be excellent candidates for catalysis and gas sensing devices. The crystallinity even in materials with average particle/grain sizes below 10 nm is very good. An average particle size of 8 nm was determined independently by HRTEM and from the fit of the line broadening. The clear presence of all crystalline maxima indicates an excellent crystallinity of the nanopowders after the preparation and without any calcination treatment.

HRTEM in combination with an Omega filter is a new technical solution to increase the analytical capabilities of transmission electron microscopy. Winterer describes the possibility to use EXAFS in combination with Reverse Monte Carlo simulation to obtain the detailed structure and elemental distribution in nanometer sized particles. By analysing the pair distribution functions of Zr-Zr, Zr-Y, and Y-Y it was shown that depending on the synthesis parameters a surface layer rich in yttrium oxide is formed instead of the expected yttrium doped zirconia. Other standard characterisation techniques were not capable to resolve the thin surface layer with a different composition. It should be pointed out that a change of the synthesis conditions resulted in a homogeneously doped oxide.

The knowledge of the detailed elemental distribution is extremely important in order to establish the structure-property relationships and to understand the complex behaviour of nanomaterials. Other frequently used characterisation techniques include nitrogen adsorption for porosity and pore size distribution, small angle neutron scattering (SANS) for particle and pore size determination, [surface analytical techniques such as Xray photoelectron spectroscopy (XPS), ion scattering spectroscopy (ISS), nuclear techniques such as Mössbauer spectroscopy and many more depending on the details of interest.

Properties in Nanostructured Materials

The interest in nanostructured materials arises from the fact that due to the small size of the building blocks and the high density of interfaces (surfaces, grain and phase boundaries) and other defects such as pores, new physical and chemical effects are expected or known properties can be improved substantially. In addition, the novel processing routes allow a bottom-up approach in materials design. In the following are the several examples of properties which are altered dramatically in the nanometer regime are presented:

Nanoparticles

The main reason for using nanoparticles is the large surface area which will be favourable for gas-solid interactions such as in catalysis and gas sensing. In addition, nanoparticles are the building blocks of bulk nanocrystalline materials, i.e., ceramics, prepared by sintering. In catalysis, alumina with a high specific surface area is used extensively as support material for catalytically active noble metals. However, the role of the substrate material was not studied extensively. For several systems it was found that the influence of the substrate material on the catalytic performance in gas reactions, such as complete oxidation of methane, can be quite drastic.

Another application of the surface reactivity of nanocrystalline oxides is in gas sensing devices. As an example, nanocrystalline titania prepared by CVS was used for gas sensing. A typical experimental arrangement consists of an alumina substrate with an interdigitised finger-like metallic structure on \one side and a resistive heater on the other side. This allows the deposition of the sensing material and the measurement of the resistivity as a function of the atmosphere.

In Figure 4, the reaction to a change of atmosphere, i.e. exposure to a different concentration of oxygen, is extremely fast, with response times (between 10 and 90 % of the total signal) in the order of less than three seconds. This compares to the response times of several minutes for commercial sensors which are based on dense thin films deposited by physical vapour deposition such as sputtering. The fast response time is an attractive feature of the nanostructured gas sensors and is a direct consequence of the nanocrystalline and nanoporous structure.

Other interesting physical effects are observed in metallic nanoparticles such as FePt prepared by a wet chemical process described by Sun et al. Fe50Pt50 nanoparticles in the size range from three to seven nanometers can be prepared with an organic coating of oleic acid which prevents the oxidation even when exposing the nanoparticles to air. The organic shell also serves to keep the nanoparticles at a molecular distance. Therefore, the nanoparticles are superparamagnetic and can be arranged on clean surfaces in regular arrays which opens interesting applications for magnetic storage devices.

Nanoceramics

Nanoceramics with grain sizes in the range of 10 to 100 nm

are typically prepared by consolidation, i.e., uniaxial compaction, cold isostatic pressing and sintering in air or vacuum. The green density, i.e. the density after initial compaction, reaches values of 40 to 50 % of the theoretical value for CVS nanopowders. The most striking feature in the case of CVS powders is the transparency of the compacted pellet.

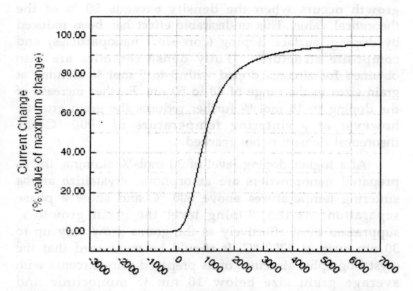

Figure 4. Change of the signal of a sensor made of nanocrystalline titania in response to a change of the oxygen concentration in the atmosphere

This is a direct consequence of the narrow size distribution of pores in the material which can only occur if no agglomerates are present in the as prepared powder or are broken up during the consolidation step. The dependence of the green density with increasing compaction pressure does not show any change in slope which would be an indication of breakage of agglomerates. The size distribution shows only pores smaller than the primary particle size. This feature is a prerequisite for a good sinterability of the CVS powders which has been found to occur in all nanoceramics under investigation (TiO_2, ZrO_2, Y_2O_3, Al_2O_3, various doped oxides etc.) at temperatures well below ½ TM.

In the intermediate sintering steps at lower temperatures, the pores disappear but no excessive pore growth is observed. However, in pure ceramics grain growth occurs when the density exceeds 90 % of the theoretical value. This undesirable effect has been reduced by doping, surface doping (core-shell nanoparticles) and composite structures. Fully dense ceramics are also obtained for zirconia doped with 3 to 5 mol % alumina at grain sizes in the range of 40 to 50 nm. Further increase of the doping to 15 mol % further reduces the grain growth; however at a sintering temperature of 1000 °C the theoretical density is not reached.

At a higher doping level of 30 mol.-% alumina, the as prepared nanopowders are amorphous, crystallize at the sintering temperatures above 600 °C and show a phase separation. At this doping level the grain growth is suppressed most effectively as the grains grow only up to 30 nm even at 1200 °C. It should be mentioned that the crystallographic structure of as prepared pure zirconia with average grain size below 10 nm is monoclinic and tetragonal, while in the alumina doped samples the tetragonal structure is stabilised.

Applications in Nanostructured Materials

Nanotechnology is already used extensively in modern industrial products. The semiconductor industry which relies on the miniaturisation of the structural components has used device structures in the nanometer range in commercial products. The time to market in this industry is extremely short as the demand by the end user is very high.

An example for the fast realisation of a technical product based on a new physical effect is the giant magneto resistance (GMR) effect originally discovered in 1985.

A few years later the first hard disks with a GMR-based read head were in the market and a revolutionary increase in storage density leading to smaller hard disks followed. Over decades several companies have marketed agglomerated powders in many industrial applications. Although the primary particle size is in the nanometer range, properties such as dispersibility, light scattering and sinterability are determined by the size of the agglomerates or aggregates.

The continued need for better products can only be fulfilled by improved materials and consequently, many companies have intensified research in this area. In developing new products companies have to consider the costs of new materials and technologies as private and industrial customers are not willing to \(buy nano, but only improved products and processes\). For the continuing support of basic science in the field of nanomaterials and nanotechnology it is of utmost importance that the new properties and technologies also lead to commercial successes.

The range of ideas for commercial products in nanomaterials is as wide as the field of materials science, covering mechanical, physical, chemical, biological, pharmaceutical, medical and cosmetic areas. Several companies have introduced into the market sun screen products based on TiO_2 and ZnO nanopowders in an attempt to reduce the amount of organic sun blockers at the same sun protection factor. An important consideration for many applications is the dispersibility of the nanopowders in various liquid (dispersions or slurries for ceramic processing) and solid media (nanocomposites) which requires surface modifications to adapt the inorganic surface to the matrix.

Ferrofluids, i.e., magnetic fluids, which have been in commercial use for many years are an example of the extremely good stability of liquid dispersions despite the strong magnetic interaction forces. Dispersions with excellent stability have been synthesised and are used in many processes. The use of nanopowders in semiconductor processing for chemical mechanical polishing (CMP) is a huge market and an important component in the manufacturing of modern integrated circuits with three-dimensional (3D) architecture. In the field of catalysis and gas sensors nanocrystalline powders and porous ceramics are considered. The development of new products by transferring basic science results has led to the foundation of numerous start-up companies as well as the involvement of large international companies in many countries.

Assembly of Nanostructures

Synthesis and assembly strategies accommodate precursors from liquid, solid, or gas phase; employ chemical or physical deposition approaches; and similarly rely on either chemical reactivity or physical compaction to integrate nanostructure building blocks within the final material structure. The "bottom-up" approach first forms the nanostructured building blocks and then assembles them into the final material. An example of this approach is the formation of powder components through aerosol techniques and then the compaction of the components into the final material. These techniques have been used extensively in the formation of structural composite materials.

One "top-down" approach begins with a suitable starting material and then "sculpts" the functionality from the material. This technique is similar to the approach used by the semiconductor industry in forming devices out of an electronic substrate (silicon), utilising pattern formation (such as electron beam lithography) and pattern transfer processes (such as reactive ion etching) that have the requisite spatial resolution to achieve creation of structures at the nanoscale.

Another top-down approach is "ball-milling," the formation of nanostructure building blocks through controlled, mechanical attrition of the bulk starting material. Those nano building blocks are then subsequently assembled into a new bulk material. In fact, many current strategies for material synthesis integrate both synthesis and assembly into a single process, such as characterises chemical synthesis of nanostructured materials.

The degree of control required over the sizes of the nanostructure components, and the nature of their distribution and bonding within the fully formed material varies greatly, depending on the ultimate materials application. Achieving selective optical absorption in a material (e.g., UVblocking dispersions) may allow a wide range of sizes of the component nanostructure building blocks, while quantum dot lasers or single electron transistors require a far tighter distribution of size of the nanostructure components. Compaction methods may provide excellent adhesion for nanocomposite materials of improved structural performance (e.g., ductility), but such interfaces may be unsatisfactory for electronic materials.

However broad the range of synthesis approaches, the critical control points fall into two categories:

1. control of the size and composition of the nanocluster components, whether they are aerosol particles, powders, semiconductor quantum dots, or other nanocomponents

2. control of the interfaces and distributions of the nanocomponents within the fully formed materials

These two aspects of nanostructure formation are inextricably linked; nevertheless, it is important to understand how to exercise separate control over the nucleation of the nanostructure building blocks and the growth (for example, minimising coagulation or agglomeration) of those components throughout the synthesis and assembly process. This latter issue is related to the importance of the following:

— the chemical, thermal, and temporal stability of such formed nanostructures

— the ability to scale-up synthesis and assembly strategies for low-cost,

— large-scale production of nanostructured materials, while at the same time maintaining control of critical feature size and quality of interfaces (economic viability is a compelling issue for any nanostructure technology)

There has been steady technological progress in all fields of nanostructure synthesis and assembly, in no small part because of the more general availability of characterisation tools having higher spatial, energy, and time resolution to clearly distinguish and trace the process of nanostructure formation. As transmission electron microscopy and X-ray diffraction techniques helped in an earlier period to relate the improved properties of "age-hardened" aluminum alloys to their nanostructure, today's technological advances in materials characterisation are providing new insights into the role of the nanostructure in determining macroscopic properties.

The tightly-coupled iteration between characterising the nanostructure, understanding the relationship between nanostructure and macroscopic material properties (Figure 5), and improved sophistication and control in determining nanostructure size and placement have accelerated the rate of progress and helped to define the critical components of this "new" field of nanostructure science and technology. Tightly focused (1-2 μm), high brightness synchrotron X-ray sources provide detailed structural information on colloids, polymers, alloys, and other material structures, highlighting the inhomogeneities of the material with suitable spatial resolution.

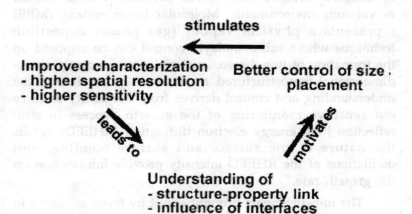

Figure 5. Interactive cycle of characterisation, understanding and enhanced control in the synthesis and assembly of nanostructures.

Another important enabling technology has been the now widely available scanning probe technology, including scanning tunnelling microscopy and atomic force microscopy. The power of these techniques has provided impetus for developing even higher performance scanning probe tips, fabricated through microfabrication techniques.

Development of different tip structures in various materials has given rise to an entire family of powerful scanning probe techniques that encompass such a wide range of characterisation capabilities that one can envision "a laboratory on a tip".The development of a tip technology also impacts the synthesis and assembly processes themselves: scanning probe technologies have been used as the basis of materials patterning and processing at nanometer scales and have provided information on the mechanical and thermal properties of materials at the nanoscale.

More sophisticated in situ monitoring strategies have provided greater understanding and control in the synthesis of nanostructured building blocks, particularly those formed in vacuum environments. Molecular beam epitaxy (MBE) represents a physical vapour (gas phase) deposition technique where sub-monolayer control can be imposed on the formation of two-dimensional and, more recently, three-dimensional nanostructured materials. A great deal of the understanding and control derives from the ability to carry out sensitive monitoring of the growth process in situ: reflection high energy electron diffraction (RHEED) details the nature of the surface and surface bonding, and oscillations of the RHEED intensity provide information on the growth rate.

The improvements brought about by these advances in technology have been substantial, but perhaps of greater importance for this nascent field of nanostructure science and technology has been the development of strategies and technologies that have been formed across the former disciplines. More reliable means of controlling nanostructure size and placement, with an end view of being able to scale up the production of such materials while maintaining the control over the nanostructure, have given impetus to a common search for novel synthesis and assembly strategies. In that search, it is apparent that the naturally occurring synthesis and assembly of biological materials can provide us with some critical insights.

Nanoparticle Synthesis

Major efforts in nanoparticle synthesis can be grouped into two broad areas: gas phase synthesis and sol-gel processing. Nanoparticles with diameters ranging from 1 to 10 nm with consistent crystal structure, surface derivatisation, and a high degree of monodispersity have been processed by both gas-phase and sol-gel techniques. Typical size variances are about 20%; however, for measurable enhancement of the quantum effect, this must be reduced to less than 5%.

Initial development of new crystalline materials was based on nanoparticles generated by evaporation and condensation (nucleation and growth) in a subatmospheric inert-gas environment. Various aerosol processing techniques have been reported to improve the production yield of nanoparticles. These include synthesis by combustion flame; plasma; laser ablation; chemical vapour condensation; spray pyrolysis; electrospray; and plasma spray. Sol-gel processing is a wet chemical synthesis approach that can be used to generate nanoparticles by gelation, precipitation, and hydrothermal treatment.

Size distribution of semiconductor, metal, and metal oxide nanoparticles can be manipulated by either dopant introduction or heat treatment. Better size and stability control of quantum-confined semiconductor nanoparticles can be achieved through the use of inverted micelles, polymer matrix architecture based on block copolymers or polymer blends, porous glasses, and ex-situ particle-capping techniques. Additional nanoparticle synthesis techniques include sonochemical processing, cavitation processing, microemulsion processing, and highenergy ball milling.

In sonochemistry, an acoustic cavitation process can generate a transient localised hot zone with extremely high temperature gradient and pressure. Such sudden changes in temperature and pressure assist the destruction of the sonochemical precursor (e.g., organometallic solution) and the formation of nanoparticles. The technique can be used to produce a large volume of material for industrial applications. In hydrodynamic cavitation, nanoparticles are generated through creation and release of gas bubbles inside the sol-gel solution. By rapidly pressurizing in a supercritical drying chamber and exposing to cavitational disturbance and high temperature heating, the sol-gel solution is mixed.

The erupted hydrodynamic bubbles are responsible for nucleation, growth, and quenching of the nanoparticles.

Particle size can be controlled by adjusting the pressure and the solution retention time in the cavitation chamber. Microemulsions have been used for synthesis of metallic, semiconductor, silica, barium sulfate, magnetic, and superconductor nanoparticles.

By controlling the very low interfacial tension ($\sim 10^{-3}$ mN/m) through the addition of a cosurfactant (e.g., an alcohol of intermediate chain length), these microemulsions are produced spontaneously without the need for significant mechanical agitation. The technique is useful for large-scale production of nanoparticles using relatively simple and inexpensive hardware. Finally, high energy ball milling, the only top-down approach for nanoparticle synthesis, has been used for the generation of magnetic, catalytic, and structural nanoparticles.

The technique, which is already a commercial technology, has been considered dirty because of contamination problems from ball-milling processes. However, the availability of tungsten carbide components and the use of inert atmosphere and/or high vacuum processes have reduced impurities to acceptable levels for many industrial applications. Common drawbacks include the low surface area, the highly polydisperse size distributions, and the partially amorphous state of the asprepared powders.

Issues in Synthesis

One of the most challenging problems in synthesis is the controlled generation of monodispersed nanoparticles with size variance so small that size selection by centrifugal precipitation or mobility classification is not necessary. Among all the synthesis techniques discussed above, gas-phase synthesis is one of the best techniques with respect to size monodispersity, typically achieved by using a combination of rigorous control of nucleationcondensation growth and avoidance of coagulation by diffusion and turbulence as well as by the effective collection of nanoparticles and their handling afterwards. The stability of the collected nanoparticle powders against agglomeration, sintering, and compositional changes can be ensured by collecting the nanoparticles in liquid suspension. For semiconducting particles, stabilisation of the liquid suspension has been demonstrated by the addition of polar solvent; surfactant molecules have been used to stabilise the liquid suspension of metallic nanoparticles.

Alternatively, inert silica encapsulation of nanoparticles by gas-phase reaction and by oxidation in colloidal solution has been shown to be effective for metallic nanoparticles. New approaches need to be developed for the generation of monodisperse nanoparticles that do not require the use of a size classification procedure. An example of this is a process developed in Japan where very monodispersed gold colloidal nanoparticles with diameters of about 1 nm have been prepared by reduction of metallic salt with UV irradiation in the presence of dendrimers.

Poly(amidoamine) dendrimers with surface amino groups of higher generations have spherical 3-D structures, which may have an effective protective action for the formation of gold nanoparticles. Although the specific role of dendrimers for the formation of monodispersed nanoparticles has yet to be defined, good monodispersity is thought to come from the complex reaction accompanying the decomposition of dendrimers, which eventually leads to the conversion of solution ions to gold nanoparticles.

Scaleup production is of great interest for nanoparticle synthesis. High energy ball milling, already a commercial high-volume process, as mentioned above, has been instrumental in generating nanoparticles for the preparation of magnetic, structural, and catalytic materials. However, the process produces polydispersed amorphous powder, which requires subsequent partial recrystallisation before the powder is consolidated into nanostructured materials. Although gas-phase synthesis is generally a low production rate process (typically in the 100 milligrams per hour range) in research laboratories, higher rates of production (about 20 grams per hour) are being demonstrated at Ångström Laboratory at Uppsala University in Sweden.

Even higher production rates (about 1 kg per hour) are now being achieved commercially. For sol-gel processing, the development of continuous processing techniques based on present knowledge of batch processing has yet to be addressed for economical scaleup production of nanoparticles. Other related sol-gel issues concern the cost of precursors and the recycling of solvent. Overall, sol-gel processing is attractive for commercial scale-up production.

A recent paradigm shift envisioned for optoelectronics and computational devices involves the assembly of molecular or quantum wires. Large polymeric molecules have been used as nano building blocks for nanoporous molecular sieves, biocompatible materials, optical switching, data processing, and other nonlinear optical components.

Chain aggregates of nanoparticles can be considered as polymer-like units with their primary particles composed of a few hundred to a few thousand molecules. Thus, these chain aggregates can be considered "heavy" quantum wires. In fact, nanoparticle chain aggregates have been studied extensively as magnetic materials, as reinforced elastomers, and as additives in concrete. These aggregates have been shown to have chemical and mechanical properties different from those of individual primary particles.

Depending on the particle size and its compositional material, the bonding force responsible for holding the aggregates together varies from weak van der Waals force for micrometer particles to strong chemical bonds for nanometer particles to very strong magnetic dipolar bonds for nanosised magnetic particles. The mechanical, optical, and electronic transport properties can be varied by controlling the diameter and the monodispersity of the primary particles, the crystalline structure and morphology, aggregate length, interfacial properties, and material purity. These chain aggregates can be formed by allowing agglomeration of nanoparticles generated by any of the synthesis techniques, with the exception of high energy ball milling, which generates particles with low surface area and high anisotropic morphologies, both of which are detrimental for the formation of chain aggregates.

Depending on the magnetic and electric charging properties of the nanoparticles, an external applied magnetic or electric field can be used to control the fractal dimension of aggregates. For optical applications of chain aggregates, lower fractal dimensions (i.e., relatively straight chain aggregates with few branches) are desirable.

Recent advances in the fabrication of nanometer fibres or tubes offer another form of building blocks for nanostructured materials. An effective way to generate nanometer fibres (or tubes) is based on the use of membrane-template techniques. Membranes, with nanochannels generated by fission-fragment tracks or by electrochemical etching of aluminum metal, are used as templates for either chemical or electrochemical deposition of conductive polymers, metal, semiconductor, and other materials for the generation of nanofibers or tubes. Since the nanochannels on membranes are very uniform in size, the diameter and the aspect ratio of the nanofibers (or tubes) synthesised by the membranetemplate technique can be precisely controlled.

This greatly facilitates the interpretation of optical data and the processing of these fibres (or tubes) into 2-D nanostructured materials. Single-crystal semiconductor nanofibers can also be grown catalytically by metalorganic vapour phase epitaxy and laser ablation vapour-liquid-solid techniques. The synthesis of these onedimensional structures with diameters in the range of 3 to 15 nm holds considerable technological promise for optoelectronic device applications, such as the p-n junctions for light emission at Hitachi Central Research Laboratory in Japan. The advent of carbon-based nanotubes has created yet another way to fabricate nanometer fibres and tubes. These nanotubes have been used as templates for the fabrication of carbide and oxide nanotubes. Synthesis of nanotubes based on BN, BC3 and BC2N have also been reported.

These nanotubes potentially possess large third-order optical non-linearity and other unusual properties. Metallic nanofibers synthesised by carbon-nanotube-template techniques are useful in the design of infrared absorption materials. The carbon nanotubes can now be catalytically produced in large quantities and have been used for reinforcement of nanostructural composite materials and concrete.

Complexity of Biological Materials

The elegant complexity of biological materials represents the achievement of structural order over many length scales, with the full structure developed from the "nested levels of structural hierarchy", in which self-assembled organic materials can form templates or scaffolding for inorganic components. These notions of a multilevel material structure with strong interactions among levels and an interplay of perfection and imperfection forming. Along with characteristic length scales, there are characteristic relaxation times of the material, bringing in the consideration of the temporal stability of the structured materials.

Deliberate strategy

"Self-assembly" is a term that by now figures prominently in the literature of nanostructured materials and nanofabrication. The term therefore carries a variety of implicit or explicit meanings. Self-assembly is a process in which supermolecular hierarchical organisation is established in a complex system of interlocking components. The mechanisms that produce the hierarchical organisation are determined by competing molecular interactions (e.g., interactions between hydrophobic versus hydrophilic components, van der Waals, Coulombic, or hydrogen bonding), resulting in particular microphase separation or surface segregation of the component materials. Thus, the use of a hierarchy of bond strengths and/or chemical specificity can produce a hierarchy of lengths in the final nanostructured material.

As one example of such self-assembled or self-organised materials, McGehee et al. have mixed silica precursors with surfactants that have self-ordered to form various surfactant-water liquid crystals, producing various structures built from walls of amorphous silica, organised about a repetitive arrangement of pores up to a hundred angstroms in diameter.

Such strategies have been adopted in synthetic formation of nanostructures, such as in the formation of networks of gold clusters. Gold clusters 3.7 nm in diameter, formed in the vapour phase, are encapsulated in organic surfactants, such as dodecanethiol, forming a colloidal suspension. The surfactants prevent the agglomeration of the gold clusters. Addition of small amount of dithiol precipitates out a 3-D cluster network, which can in turn be deposited onto another solid substrate.

The methodology of self-assembly has even been extended to physical vapour deposition processes where it would seem more difficult to control the nucleation and growth of three-dimensional nanostructures. Utilising the strain inherent in the epitaxial growth of lattice-mismatched materials, and the expected strain-induced transition from two-dimensional (layered) to three-dimensional (islanded) growth, together with careful monitoring of the growth process through RHEED analysis, researchers have been able to form arrays of semiconductor quantum dots, ~200-300 Å in diameter, ~1011 cm² in density, and with a size variation of about ±7%.

Figure 6. TEM images of (a) the lamellar morphology, (b) the cubic phase with Ia3d symmetry viewed along its zone axis, and (c) the hexagonal phase viewed along its [001] zone axis of thesilica/surfactant nanostructured composites by co-assembly (bars = 30 nm).

An example of such "self-assembled" semiconductor quantum dots is shown in Figure 7. The achievement of arrays of several billions of quantum dots of these dimensions with such a size variation is beyond the capability of standard high resolution lithographic and pattern transfer processes.

Moreover, the controlled formation of critical surfaces and interfaces without the intercession of ion-assisted processing that can introduce potential defects into the materials has produced a rich source of optically and electronically efficient quantum structures. A number of researchers have already incorporated such self-assembled dots into laser structures.

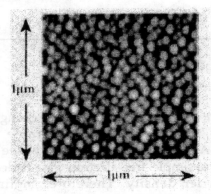

Figure 7. Array of InAs quantum dot structures grown on GaAs substrates

Chemical specificity may provide the most robust means of ensuring control of size and placement of nanostructured building blocks, and recent work in the synthesis of compound semiconductor quantum dots from chemical precursors have provided even tighter distributions of size variation (±5%) than those shown in the strain-induced self-assembled dots.

7

Magnetic Nanostructures

The wavefunction of electrons is going to change when they are confined to dimensions comparable with their wavelength. As an estimate we may see the Fermi wavelength of a simple free-electron gas. It decreases with increasing carrier density. Therefore, confinement and quantisation phenomena are visible in semiconductors already at dimensions greater than 200 nm, whereas in metals they typically are seen at 1 nm. In fact, the Fermi wavelength of typical metals has atomic dimensions, but beat frequencies with the lattice can be an order of magnitude larger.

A related way of reasoning considers the formation of low-dimensional electronic states by quantisation. Confining electrons to small structures causes the continuous bulk bands to split up into discrete levels, for example quantum well states in a slab. For N atomic layers in the slab there are N levels. In order to exhibit two-dimensional behaviour there should be only a single level within ± kT of the Fermi level. Several levels within the Fermi cut-off would already approach a three-dimensional continuum. For a coarse estimate of the corresponding slab thickness, one may set the energy E of the lowest level equal to kT. For room temperature (E = kT = 0.026 eV), one obtains a de Broglie wavelength $\lambda = h/p = h/(2mE)^{1/2} \approx 1.23$ nm/(E /eV)$^{1/2} \approx 8$ nm, which is comparable with the spatial extent of the lowest quantum state. Thus, both the high electron density in magnetic metals and the requirement of room-temperature operation for quantum devices point to dimensions of a few nanometres.

Fabrication

Equilibrium growth

For growing magnetic layers with monolayer control it is important to realise the forces that rearrange the growing surface. A dominant role is played by the free energies γ of the surface and interface. The morphology of material B grown on material A depends on the balance between the free surface energies of substrate, overlayer and interface. If

$$\gamma_{\text{substrate}} > \gamma_{\text{overlayer}} + \gamma_{\text{interface}}, \tag{1}$$

the first atomic layer wants to coat the whole surface to provide optimum energy reduction. For subsequent layers the situation has changed; the surface energy of their substrate has already been reduced by the first layer and they do not experience the same interface energy. In addition, they have to absorb the misfit strain energy, which grows with increasing film thickness. Therefore, a continued layer-by-layer mode is rare, and the more common mode is the formation of islands on top of a flat first layer. For example, Cu on bcc Fe(100) breaks up into large islands after first wetting the surface. This mode leaves as much as possible of the energetically favourable first layer exposed and reduces strain because the islands are able to relax laterally. If the energy balance at the interface is tipped the opposite way, that is for

$$\gamma_{\text{substrate}} < \gamma_{\text{overlayer}} + \gamma_{\text{interface}} \tag{2}$$

the overlayer has a tendency to nucleate three-dimensional islands right away, and leave the low-energy substrate exposed. This situation generally occurs when growing magnetic materials on top of an inert substrate, such as a noble metal or an oxide. If the substrate atoms are mobile enough, they tend to trade places with the deposited magnetic atoms, which blurs the interface. Magnetic materials exhibit a relatively high surface energy, owing to their partially filled d shell.

A brief anneal recrystallises the film before surface diffusion begins and islands are formed. This technique has been used to obtain smooth films by suppressing Stranski-Krastanov growth. An example is the deposition of smooth Gd films on Wat room temperature with a 530K post-anneal. For reactive materials, such as rare earths and early transition metals, such epitaxial films have better surfaces than single crystals. This method is applicable to noble metals, too. The smoothest Cu-Co(100) interfaces are obtained that way, and atomically flat Ag films have been grown on GaAs in this fashion. Smooth growth can be promoted by a surfactant, that is a coating that floats on top of the growing film without being incorporated into it. Surfactants promote layer-by-layer growth in a variety of ways.

Lowering the surface energy is the most obvious, but there are other possibilities, such as lowering of the barrier for diffusion of adatoms down from islands and introducing a high density of nuclei for growing monolayer islands. Several boundary conditions are imposed on a surfactant, for example low surface energy, high mobility and little reactivity with the growing film. Therefore, only a few surfactants are known for use with the highly reactive ferromagnets, for example O, N, CO for Fe, CO for Fe, Au for Fe and Pb for Co. Cu and Ag exhibit low surface energy and little miscibility with ferromagnets, for example equilibrium concentrations of less than 1% in Fe and Co and vice versa. The interface energy comes into play when two materials are highly miscible. Cr forms alloys with Fe, leading to a strong tendency for Cr to be incorporated into Fe near the interface. The growth of Fe/Cr layers is dominated by the strongly attractive interface energy. In many metal-on-metal systems, one finds that the first few atomic layers are growing layer by layer but eventually break up into islands owing to misfit strain.

Strain grows with increasing film thickness and leads to the sudden formation of misfit dislocations at a critical thickness that depends mainly on the lattice mismatch. For a 1-2% mismatch it takes 10 nm or more for this break-up to occur, and for 4-6%mismatch only a couple of atomic layers. Therefore, one is always looking out for lattice-matched materials combinations in order to produce perfect epitaxial films. As shown in table 1, there are two principal groups of lattice-matched materials, one containing bcc Fe, Cr(100), fcc Ag, Au(100), Ge and GaAs(100), and the other based on fcc Fe, Co, Ni and Cu.

Table 1. Lattice-matched combinations of magnetic materials, substrates and spacer layers.

First group:			
Magnetic metal	Cr (bcc)	Fe (bcc)	Co (bcc)
$2^{1/2}a$ [Å] (a [Å])	4.07 (2.88)	4.05 (2.87)	3.99 (2.82)
Simple or noble	Al	Ag	Au
metal a [Å]	4.05	4.09	4.07
Semiconductor	Ge	GaAs	ZnSe
$a/2^{1/2}$ [Å] (a [Å])	3.99 (5.65)	4.00 (5.65)	4.01 (5.67)
Insulator	LiF	NaCl	MgO
a [Å] $a/2^{1/2}$ [Å]	4.02 (2.84)	3.99 (5.65)	4.20 (2.97)
Second group:			
Material	Fe (fcc)	Co (fcc)	Ni (fcc) Cu Diamond
a [Å]	3.59	3.55	3.52 3.61 3.57

For some of these materials the match is not 1:1 but $2^{1/2}$:1 which makes it possible to obtain atom-on-atom registry between a fcc(100) surface and a bcc(100) surface that has $2^{1/2}$ smaller lattice constant and is rotated azimuthally by 45°.

The thermodynamic laws of film growth are too restrictive for growing the desired variety of magnetic structures. Most of the interesting structures do not occur naturally, and will disintegrate when annealed to temperatures higher than about 200°C. Interfaces become washed out by interdiffusion, surfaces of magnetic layers become coated with noble metal atoms diffusing out from the substrate, continuous films break up into platelets, and metastable phases such as fcc Fe and fcc Co convert to their stable counterparts bcc Fe and hcp Co.

A skilled film grower has a variety of non-equilibrium tricks in his bag, and more are being discovered continuously. This is an area where science and art meet. As a consequence, non-equilibrium growth methods have to be considered which operate at reduced temperature or increased deposition rate.

At high temperatures the adsorbed atoms diffuse to the nearest step, where they find the bonding site with the highest coordination and become incorporated. This is the step-flow growth mode. At reduced temperatures, or higher rates, or lower step densities, the arriving atoms do not have enough time to find the nearest step edge and nucleate spontaneously into islands. These islands grow by incorporating atoms that arrive nearby and eventually coalesce into a smooth monolayer. This is a popular growth mode, since it makes it easy to count the growing monolayers one by one. The periodic change in surface roughness from smooth at integer-monolayer coverage to rough at half-integer-monolayer coverage gives rise to oscillations in the diffraction intensity for electrons, ions and X-rays.

The effect can be enhanced by going to the out-of-phase condition, where the beam reflected from the upper terrace interferes destructively with that from the lower terrace. Ideally, they cancel out to zero at half-integer coverage. By following the amplitude of the oscillations, one finds a complex growth behaviour with two abrupt changes at four and 11 monolayers. The change at 11 monolayers is due to metastable fcc Fe converting into ordinary bcc Fe. It can be delayed by using adsorbed CO as surfactant.

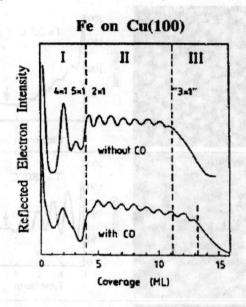

Figure 1. Oscillations in the intensity of a reflected electron beam in reflection high-energy electron diffraction (RHEED).

At the lowest growth temperatures the arriving atoms nucleate islands on top of each other, giving rise to rather rough topographies. In this regime, diffusion along step edges and across step edges becomes an important parameter, in addition to the diffusion on top of terraces. A recently developed non-equilibrium technique for growing films with monolayer control is atomic layer epitaxy. This 'digital' growth method consists of two reaction steps per layer.

First, a monolayer of molecules is adsorbed on the surface under conditions where the second layer does not stick. Then the surface is reactivated by driving passivating ligands off, using a chemical reaction, light or a temperature pulse.

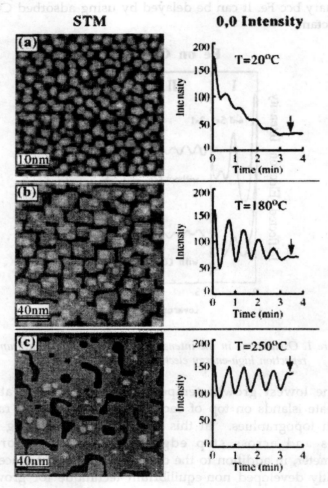

Figure 2. STM picture of Fe growing on Fe(100) in various growth modes at di. erent temperatures.

Such processes have been successful for semiconductors. For magnetic materials, one could consider carbonyls or aromatic compounds, such as ferrocene and bis-benzene chromium. With carbonyls, there is a strong tendency towards incorporating carbon and oxygen into the reactive ferromagnets. Electrochemical deposition allows deposition at room temperature under nearequilibrium conditions, which should be ideal for obtaining sharp interfaces. Its application to magnetic layers with monolayer control is just beginning.

Interfaces

An important aspect of growing magnetic multilayers has been the quality of the interfaces, that is lateral smoothness and vertical sharpness. For example, the formation of quantised electronic states is dependent on interfaces that are smoother than the wavelength of the electrons, just as standing waves in an optical interferometer require mirrors smoother than the wavelength of the light.

The magnetoresistance in magnetic multilayers has been found to depend on the interface roughness, sometimes increasing and sometimes decreasing with increasing roughness. The sharpness of an interface is governed by interdiffusion and chemical reaction. Some noble metals and ferromagnets have a large miscibility gap in the phase diagram, such as Fe-Cu, Fe-Ag and Co-Cu.

Others form alloys, such as Ni-Cu and Fe-Au. While noble metals have little effect on ferromagnetic properties, other elements have greater effect. Arsenic, for example, diffuses into a growing Fe film on GaAs(100), which is lattice matched to Fe. The first 10 nm of Fe lose part of their magnetic moment, and the interface is magnetically dead. Thicker epitaxial Fe films on GaAs (in the micrometre range) have excellent magnetic properties, and similarly on the lessreactive ZnSe already at 10 nm thickness. S passivation of the GaAs surface is able to suppress As outdiffusion and allows high-quality Fe films in the nanometre regime. Si as a substrate presents similar problems, since it reacts with most magnetic materials to form silicides. On the other hand, semiconductor substrates are highly desirable for magnetic multilayers since they do not short out the current flowing through a magnetic multilayer and are readily available and processed. As a consequence, there has been extensive work on buffer layers that prevent undesirable out-diffusion and reaction with the substrate, for example, S, Ge, Cr, Ag and Au buffers on GaAs and Ge and Cu, Cr on Si. Insulators, such as MgO(100), MgO(110) and Al2O3(0001) are being used as substrates for epitaxial growth of various low-index surface, using metal seed layers.

Wires

An entry into the one-dimensional world can be gained by growth at stepped surfaces. Fairly regular step arrays can be produced on vicinal metal and semiconductor surfaces. For obtaining the straightest possible steps, one needs to select the most stable azimuthal step orientation, usually consisting of close-packed atom rows. On silicon, it is now possible to obtain steps with only one kink in 20000 lattice sites.

They form the boundaries of islands during equilibrium growth. Steps provide a template for attaching stripes or wires by step flow growth. Analogues to all the threedimensional growth modes reappear in lower dimensions, such as layer-by-layer, Stranski-Krastanov and island growth.

On W(110), however, only the first row of Cu atoms decorates the step edge, and additional Cu grows in monolayer-height islands that are attached to the step edges, analogous to Stranski-Krastanov growth. The analogue of island growth has been observed for Co on stepped Cu(111), where Co islands nucleate at the step edges and eventually coalesce higher coverage.

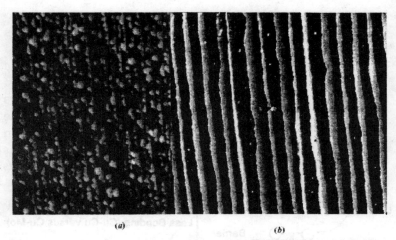

(a) *(b)*

Figure 3. Growth modes in two dimensions. Cu (a) on stepped W(110) and (b) on Mo(110) displays the analogue of Stranski-Krastanov and layer-by-layer growth.

Such a growth mode can be expected in general when attempting to grow the highenergy ferromagnets on low energy substrates, such as noble metals and insulators. An additional phenomenon at stepped surfaces is a barrier for crossing steps. This is obvious for an uphill crossing, since the atom incorporated at the step edge would be less coordinated on the terrace, but even in the downhill direction there is a temporary loss of neighbours when crossing the step edge. An atom exchange mechanism can eliminate this barrier during homoepitaxy on certain metals.

In a heteroepitaxial system, such as Cu/Mo(110) in figure 3, the Cu atom crossing a Mo-Cu boundary trades Mo neighbours for Cu neighbours, which provide less binding energy. The wider the terrace that a Cu stripe resides on, the wider is the stripe. Apparently, the Cu atoms are swept towards the uphill edge of an individual terrace. It requires higher annealing temperatures to let atoms travel across step edges and obtain a uniform stripe width, independent of terrace width.

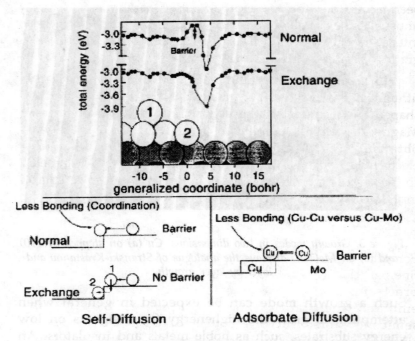

Figure 4. Diffusion across step edges.

The existence of such a uniform stripe width despite non-uniform terrace width indicates that the binding energy increases towards the step edge in this case. In order to make step decoration a widely applicable technique it has been proposed to use a two-step process. In the first step, a template of inert stripes is grown by step decoration. In the second step, the desired material is grown by selective chemical vapour deposition on the remaining parts of the reactive substrate. In addition to step decoration there are various other mechanisms that lead to spontaneous formation of wires and stripes, for example growth on anisotropic surfaces.

Deposited atoms diffuse parallel to atom rows at the fcc (110) surface, but not perpendicular. Adsorbates have been found to selforganise into stripes on such surfaces. An unusual patterning method uses the interference field of an intense laser to focus a beam of Cr atoms into a regular grating with line widths down to the 40 nm range.

Lithographic patterning and side evaporation onto lithographic steps have been used to produce sawtooth-shaped Si substrates for the deposition of magnetic stripes. Magnetic wires perpendicular to the surface have been obtained by filling pores in a polymer film with electroplated metals. Both of these structures are designed to achieve higher magnetoresistance than in planar multilayers.

Particles

For growing zero-dimensional magnetic structures, that is fine particles with uniform size, one may either consider the processing methods for particles in magnetic tapes or emulate the fabrication of 'quantum dots' on semiconductors. Dots are expected to exhibit the most singular behaviour among low-dimensional structures, but they also present the highest difficulty in connecting them to the macroscopic world, for example by nanometre-sized electrical contacts, by optical read-out or by remotely sensing an electric or magnetic field.

The processing of magnetic particles for magnetic tapes has experienced a long development of ever more sophisticated processing methods. In order to achieve high coercive fields, that is high stability, these particles are grown needle-shaped (acicular) with a typical length of 0.5 µm and width of 0.1 µm. Initially, seed particles 10 nm long of $Fe(OH)_2$ are precipitated from a $FeSO_4$ solution by adding NH_4.

Controlled ripening and reduction-oxidation cycles eventually produce particles consisting of Fe_2O_3 or Fe with special coatings that serve as chemical protection and shape the magnetic properties. With semiconductors, highly homogeneous nanocrystals have been obtained by seeding in a supersaturated solution, followed by controlled ripening with passivation layers and size-selective precipitation. The size distribution is better than 4%, which is close to monolayer control.

The surface analogue of seeding plus ripening consists of nucleating seeds with the critical nucleus size by deposition at low temperature, where atoms are immobile. The size of these seeds is increased in controlled fashion at somewhat higher temperature, where they sweep in adatoms within a diffusion length. A regular array of misfit dislocations can serve as a template for nucleation of dots.

A similar nucleation has been found on reconstructed metal surfaces with dislocations, built in either by an intrinsic reconstruction or by a mismatched adsorbate layer. On the low end of the particle size spectrum we have clusters of a few atoms and magnetic molecules. Cluster research has brought about several techniques for obtaining microscopic quantities of mass-selected clusters. An iron target is vaporised by a laser, injecting hot Fe atoms and ions into a He carrier gas, where they condense and ripen into clusters of a few atoms in size.

Supersonic expansion of the carrier gas produces a cold cluster beam that can be mass selected. Interesting magnetic molecules, such as the 'ferric-wheel' or ferritin proteins can be synthesised directly. Small magnetic particles are also encountered in biological systems, for example Fe stored in the spleen and magnetic field sensors in fish and bacteria.

All the growth methods discussed so far rely on parallel processing or selfassembly. For example, decorating step edges of a vicinal surface produces 10^6 wires per cm^2 simultaneously. This is the economical way to produce a macroscopic amount of material. However, there are limitations. It is impossible to write custom patterns, and one has to cope with a finite size distribution, for example in the width of wires or the diameter of dots. For writing structures down to a scale of about 200 nm it is feasible to use optical lithography. Electron-beam lithography reaches 15 nm. Such techniques have been used to produce magnetic wires, as well as dots. For writing structures with atomic perfection there is the possibility of moving atoms or molecules with the tip of a scanning tunnelling microscope (STM). Crommie et al. arranged Fe atoms into a corral on a Cu(111) surface (figure 5). The idea is to approach the adatom close enough that the force holding it to the tip overcomes the lateral forces when moving across surface corrugations.

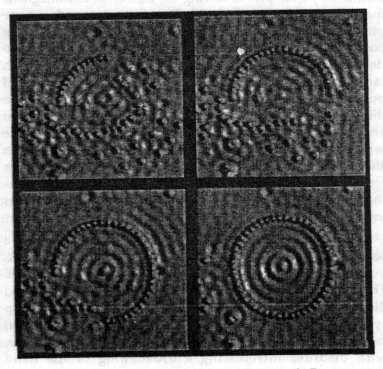

Figure 5. Construction of a quantum corral from single Fe atoms on a Cu(111) surface.

On the other hand, the tip force should be weaker than the bond to the surface, such that the atom does not end up on the tip. Such controlled atom movement has been achieved only at low temperatures so far. There have been successful efforts to move larger entities, such as organic molecules at room temperature. STMhas also been used on a much larger scale to produce 50 nm lines and dots by cracking Ni and Fe carbonyls with the electrons emitted from an STM tip.

Characterisation of Electronic Structure

Among the wide variety of techniques that are available to measure these quantities we illustrate the most common methods by examples involving the elemental ferromagnetic materials Fe, Co, Ni and Gd. Photoemission and inverse photoemission are the standard techniques for probing occupied and unoccupied electronic states respectively. To determine magnetic properties, on the other hand, a much larger arsenal of techniques is required. Conventional bulksensitive techniques, such as neutron scattering, have difficulties detecting the small amount of magnetic material encountered in nanostructures. To improve surface sensitivity it is useful to utilise probing particles with a short penetration depth, such as low-energy electrons. For reaching nanometre spatial resolution in all dimensions there are a number of innovative magnetic microscopies under development.

Electrons in a solid are completely characterised by a set of quantum numbers. These are energy E, momentum k, point-group symmetry (i.e. angular symmetry) and spin. This information can be summarised by plotting E(k) band dispersions with the appropriate labels for point-group symmetry and spin. Disordered solids (e.g. random alloys) can be characterised by average values of these quantities, with disorder introducing a broadening of the band dispersions.

PHOTOEMISSION

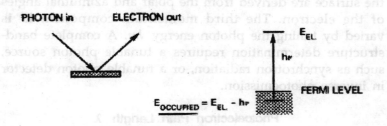

INVERSE PHOTOEMISSION

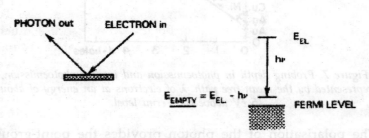

Figure 6. Photoemission and inverse photoemission

Localised electronic states exhibit flat E(k) band dispersions, for example in ionic compounds or in the 4f levels of rare earths. A complete set of quantum numbers is obtainable from photoemission and its time-reversed counterpart, that is, inverse photoemission (figure 6). The former probes occupied states, and the latter unoccupied states.

How are energy band dispersions determined? A first look at the task reveals that photoemission (and inverse photoemission) provides just the right number of independent measurable variables to establish a unique correspondence to the quantum numbers of an electron is a solid. The energy E is obtained from the kinetic energy of the electron. The two momentum components $k^{||}$ parallel to the surface are derived from the polar and azimuthal angles of the electron. The third momentum component $k^{\wedge}$ is varied by tuning the photon energy hn. A complete band-structure determination requires a tunable photon source, such as synchrotron radiation, or a tunable photon detector in inverse photoemission.

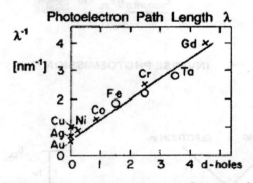

Figure 7. Probing depth in photoemission and inverse photoemission, represented by the mean free path λ of electrons at an energy of about 5 eV above the Fermi level.

The polarisation of the photon provides the point-group symmetry, and the spin polarisation of the electron the spin quantum number. For two-dimensional states in thin films and at surfaces the determination of energy bands is almost trivial since only E and $k^{||}$ have to be determined. These quantities obey the conservation laws

$$E_l = E_u - hv \qquad (3)$$

and

$$k^{||}_l = k^{||}_u - g^{||}, \qquad (4)$$

where $g^{||}$ is a vector of the reciprocal surface lattice, u denotes the upper state and l the lower state.

These conservation laws can be derived from the invariance of the crystal with respect to translation in time and in space (by a surface lattice vector). For the photon, only its energy *hn* appears in the balance because the momentum of an ultraviolet photon is negligible compared with the momentum of the electrons.

The subtraction of a reciprocal lattice vector simply corresponds to plotting energy bands in a reduced surface Brillouin zone, i.e. within the unit cell in ki space. These are the rules of band-mapping in a nutshell. The d bands are narrower than the s, p band because d states are more localised, giving less overlap between adjacent atoms and a smaller energy spread between bonding and antibonding combinations of d states. As the atomic number increases from Fe to Co and Ni, the d bands become increasingly filled and move down below the Fermi level. Gd exhibits additional *f* states, which are so localised that they do not exhibit any measaurable band dispersion.

Since the f shell is half-filled and fully polarised in Gd, one has an occupied f level with majority spin, as well as an unoccupied *f* level with minority spin. The seemingly complex set of d bands can be fitted by a rather small set of parameters by combined interpolation schemes, which combine a tight-binding approach for the d bands with plane waves for the s, p bands. In order to measure the energy of an electron it is necessary to excite it above the Fermi level. Such an excitation produces a response from the surrounding electrons, for example multielectron excitations and screening. Two-electron excitations lead to a narrowing of the 3d band and reduce the magnetic exchange splitting, for example as much as 30% band narrowing and a factor of $\frac{1}{2}$ in the magnetic splitting. The two-electron excitations show up directly as satellites below the single-electron bands, for example the 6 eV satellite in Ni.

These excited-state effects are strongest in Ni, weaker in Co and barely perceptible in Fe. Theoretical methods do exist that take excited-state effects into account systematically from first principles. Such quasiparticle calculations have been very successful for semiconductors but are just becoming feasible for d and f electrons in magnetic materials. In the absence of such first-principles calculations we provide empirical band structures as a starting point for describing electronic states at surfaces, thin films and nanostructures.

Magnetic exchange splitting

For ferromagnets the bands are split into two subsets: one with majority spin, and the other with minority spin. The magnetic exchange splitting δE_{ex} between majority and minority spin bands is the key to magnetism. Owing to the exchange splitting the minority spin band is filled less than the majority band, thus creating the spin imbalance that produces the magnetic moment. Therefore, one might expect the moment to increase with the exchange splitting. For example, the values of δE_{ex} in Fe, Co and Ni are 1.8-2.4 eV, 0.93-1.05 eV and 0.17-0.33 eV respectively.

The corresponding moments are 2.2μB, 1.7μB and 0.6μB respectively. Most of the moment is carried by the 3d electrons (about 110%), whereas the s, p electrons are weakly polarised in the opposite direction (about—10% of the total moment). For Gd, one has a total moment of 7.6μB carried mostly by the 4f electrons (7μB), with the 5d electrons contributing 0.6 m B. The exchange splitting is δE_{ex} = 12.4 eV for the 4f states and δE_{ex} = 0.8eV for the 5d states. There is some variation in δE_{ex} with momentum k, which appears to be mainly tied to the symmetry of the bands.

Bands with t_{2g} ($\Gamma_{25'}$, X_5) symmetry have a larger splitting than those with e_g ($\Gamma_{12'}$, X_2) symmetry, for example 0.33 eV as against 0.17 eV in Ni. This variation blurs the expected correlation between δE_{ex} and the magnetic moment.

Nevertheless, the momentum and symmetry-averaged value of δE_{ex} turns out to be an indicator of the local magnetic moment for 3d transition metals, not only for ferromagnets but also for antiferromagnets and, in the absence of long-range order, for spin glasses and free atoms. As an empirical rule of thumb, the 3d moment is about 1µB per electron volt exchange splitting. This trend provides a quick first look at the size of the local moments in thin-film and monolayer systems.

For delocalised band-like states, such as in Cr, the splittings occur around the points in momentum space that correspond to the reciprocal-lattice vectors of the antiferromagnetic spin ordering. For example, along the direction of the alternating spins the antiferromagnetic splitting occurs half-way out to the Brillouin zone boundary of the atomic lattice. The doubling of the unit cell in real space by the spin lattice halves the unit cell in momentum space, and the magnetic interaction opens up bandgaps at the magnetic Brillouin zone boundary.

The upper state corresponds to a spin-down electron at a spin-up site and vice versa, and the lower state to a spin-up electron at a spin-up site and vice versa. The situation is similar to that in a ferromagnet when considering the spin polarisation at a particular atom; local minority states are at higher energy than local majority states. Optical data give a magnetic splitting of 0.13 eV for pure Cr which exhibits a slightly incommensurate magnetic period. The splitting increases to 0.36 eV when the antiferromagnetism becomes commensurate by 1% Mn or Re doping.

In antiferromagnets with localised states the bands have little E(k) dispersion and the splitting extends throughout most of the Brillouin zone. Magnetic excitations can also be described by an E(k), where E and k are energy and momentum transfer respectively. One may classify them into single- and many-electron excitations. The fundamental single-electron excitation is a transition between bands of opposite spin. It requires a minimum energy Δ in ferromagnets with a filled majority spin band, such as Co and Ni ('strong ferromagnets').

It is 0.35 eV in Co—from E_F to $L_{3'}$ Γ_5 and 0.11 eV in Ni—from E_F to X_5. Fe lacks such a gap since the top of the majority spin band lies above the Fermi level—0.12 eV for H_{25}. At zero momentum transfer the energy of the spin-flip excitations corresponds to the magnetic exchange splitting δE_{ex}. That can be probed by spin-polarised electron-energy loss spectroscopy. The fundamental many-electron excitation is a spin wave. Spin waves are low-energy excitations.

They start out with a parabolic $E(k)$ dispersion at $k = 0$ and broaden out when they begin to overlap with single-electron excitations above the Stoner gap. Many of these single- and manyelectron excitations become thermally accessible near the Curie temperature, making finite-temperature calculations of the band structure and of the Curie temperature rather challenging. Special spin-wave modes develop at surfaces and in multilayers owing to the altered boundary conditions.

Magnetism

Magnetism reflects the underlying band structure. The magnetic moment is given by the difference between the filling of majority and minority spin bands, which is directly related to the ferromagnetic exchange splitting between the bands. Total energy minimisation over all occupied band states yields crystal structure and magnetic ordering.

In a somewhat oversimplified atomic orbital picture, the moment is created by interaction between electrons on the same atom and the coupling between electrons on different atoms. Spins are aligned antiparallel at the smallest distances or volumes, since Pauli's exclusion principle prevents equal spins from occupying the same spot. This reduces the moment of an individual atom and produces antiferromagnetic coupling between atoms. The interaction changes its sign as soon as the wavefunctions cease to overlap strongly. The moment increases and the coupling becomes ferromagnetic. At even larger distances the magnetic coupling becomes indirect, using conduction electrons as mediators.

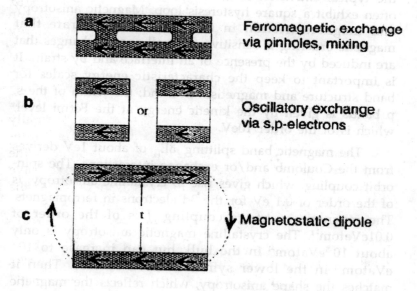

Figure 8. Coupling between magnetic layers (▦)ia non-magnetic spacers of varying thickness t ( ).

It oscillates with a period determined by Fermi wave-vectors, thereby bringing orientation-dependent Fermi surface parameters into the picture. More sophisticated treatments, such as local density theory, take the band-like (itinerant) nature of the 3d wavefunctions in metallic ferromagnets into account, which blurs the simple atomic picture. There is much more to magnetism than the spin-split band structure. Magnetic domains provide a large-scale texture that adds enormous complexity. As a consequence, there are many more magnetic properties than band-structure parameters, and a large number of techniques to measure them.

The variability of an H(M) hysteresis loop reflects a complex domain structure. Interestingly, the situation becomes simpler in nanostructures, which are smaller than the typical extension of a domain wall (0.1-1 μm). They often exhibit a square hysteresis loop. Magnetic anisotropy and magnetostriction in thin films demonstrate that magnetic ordering is sensitive to small energy changes that are induced by the presence of an interface and by strain. It is important to keep the characteristic energy scales for band structure and magnetism in mind; the width of the s, p bands is given by the kinetic energy at the Fermi level, which is of the order 10eV.

The magnetic band splitting δE_{ex} of about 1eV derives from the Coulomb and/or exchange interactions. The spin-orbit coupling, which gives rise to crystalline anisotropy, is of the order of 0.1 eV for the 3d electrons in ferromagnets. The magnetic exchange coupling J is of the order of $0.01 eVatom^{-1}$. The crystalline magnetic anisotropy is only about $10^{-5} eVatom^{-1}$ in the bulk but can increase to 10^{-4} $eVatom^{-1}$ in the lower symmetry of a surface. Then it matches the shape anisotropy, which reflects the magnetic dipole-dipole interaction.

Magnetic properties

Magnetisation and magnetic coupling are calculable from first principles by band theory. Today, the most common approach uses the local density formalism, where the spin-dependent part of the total energy is approximated by an expression derived from an electron gas. The corresponding exchange-correlation potential $V_{xc} = V_x + V_c$ depends only on the majority and minority spin densities $\rho\uparrow$ and $\rho\downarrow$. The dominant part is the exchange potential V_x, which is proportional to $-\rho\uparrow^{1/3}$ and $-\rho\downarrow^{1/3}$ for majority and minority spin wavefunctions respectively.

Different magnetic structures, such as paramagnetic, ferromagnetic and various antiferromagnetic configurations, exhibit different total energies, and the lowest-energy configuration obtained by local density theory represents the observed magnetic state in most cases. Ferromagnetism occurs in rather few elements, Fe, Co, Ni, Gd and a few rare earths with low Curie temperatures (many fewer than superconductors). The stability of ferromagnetism in these elements can be explained by the Stoner criterion, which takes the density $D(E_F)$ of states at the Fermi level and an atomic exchange integral I as input. The transition from paramagnetism to ferromagnetism becomes favourable if

$$D(E_F). \ I > 1. \tag{5}$$

Then the system can lower its energy by bringing enough majority spin electrons down in energy by opening up the ferromagnetic exchange splitting. As with the opening of a gap in superconductivity, the density of states at the Fermi level and a coupling parameter (here the exchange integral I) are the critical quantities. The Stoner criterion explains why Fe, Co and Ni are singled out for ferromagnetism several other elements are close to fulfilling the criterion, for example Pd. In some thin-film structures these elements are transformed into ferromagnets, for example V, Cr, Mn, Mo, Ru, Rh, Pd and Pt.

Magnetism can either be induced by exchange coupling to a ferromagnetic substrate or occur spontaneously owing to a higher density of states in a monolayer, caused by reduced bandwidth. Antiferromagnetism is also driven by a large density of states at the Fermi level, but in this case at specific points in k space that are related to the antiferromagnetic reciprocal-lattice vector. The antiferromagnetic ordering opens a bandgap E_g at these k-points that lowers the energy of the occupied states at the bottom of the gap and removes the high density of states from the Fermi level. Again, one discovers similarities with the opening of a gap in superconductivity. In fact, antiferromagnetic order in Cr can be mapped onto the superconducting order parameter to a certain approximation. The Bardeen-Cooper-Schrieffer theory of superconductivity then produces a relation between critical temperature and gap E_g:

$$E_g \approx 3.5kT_{N'eel}. \tag{6}$$

This relation is only a rough guide, as the case of Cr shows, where a N'eel temperature of 311K and a gap of 0.13 eV give Eg $\approx$ 5kTN'eel. At elevated temperatures it becomes rather difficult to calculate magnetic properties from first principles, particularly the Curie and the Neel temperatures. The complex time-dependent magnetic microstructure near the critical temperature presents a formidable challenge. In the atomic limit, for example using the Heisenberg model, one assumes a magnetic moment on each atom that persists beyond T_C.

The magnetisation vanishes by orienting the moments at random in the paramagnetic phase. The other extreme, that is the Stoner model of band-like ferromagnetism, assumes that the magnetic moment gradually decreases at elevated temperature and vanishes above T_C. It gives Curie temperatures twice as high as observed. The basic flaw is the assumption that the magnetic order disappears by spin-flip excitations across the Stoner gap Δ. They cost more energy than is actually needed to disorder magnetic moments. More realistic models contain small domains with local order whose orientations are starting to fluctuate when approaching the Curie temperature T_C. Some degree of local correlation remains even above T_C.

Such a picture brings in spin-wave excitations (magnons) which are not contained in the ground-state energy bands. Recent efforts to model the spin structure just below and above the Curie point from first principles give qualitatively correct Curie temperatures. At surfaces, an increased T_C becomes possible owing to the higher density of states at the Fermi level. In thin films, T_C generally decreases owing to fewer magnetic neighbours. The magnetic moment is dominated by the electrons with high angular momentum, the 3d electrons in Cr, Mn, Fe, Co, Ni' and the 4f electrons in the rare earths. With increasing atomic volume, one approaches the free-atom limit where Hund's first rule postulates maximum spin, that is all the individual spins of the electrons in a shell are aligned parallel.

Electrons with parallel spin have different spatial wavefunctions, owing to Pauli's exclusion principle which is reflected in the exchange interaction. That reduces their Coulomb repulsion. When the atoms are squeezed into a solid, some of the electrons are rorced into common spatial wavefunctions which forces their spins antiparallel and reduces the overall magnetic moment. For example, the moment of $5\mu B$ in the free Cr atom is reduced by an order of magnitude in the solid.

At surfaces and interfaces, and in thin films the atomic volume is able to expand, which allows part of the atomic moment to be recovered. Another consequence of the volume-dependent magnetic moment is magnetostriction, that is, a change in the magnetisation with strain and vice versa. This effect severely affects the functioning of magnetic devices as they become smaller and are able to sustain ever higher strain. Therefore magnetic devices are often composed of alloys with zero first-order magnetostriction, such as permalloy ($Ni_{0.8}Fe_{0.2}$) or analogous ternary compounds (along the line $Ni_{0.8}Fe_{0.2}$-$Ni_{0.65}Co_{0.35}$ and along $Ni_{0.25}Co_{0.3}Fe_{0.45}$-$Ni_{0.05}Co_{0.9}Fe_{0.05}$).

In strained epitaxial layers the magnetic ordering may change completely, for example from ferromagnetic to antiferromagnetic in thin Fe films on Cu(100). Magnetic coupling between spins on different atoms determines the magnetic order, for example ferromagnetic as against antiferromagnetic in bulk solids. Magnetic multilayers exhibit analogous configurations, where the magnetisations of two layers lie parallel or antiparallel to each other, while each layer exhibits ferromagnetic order internally. The overall magnetic configuration can be analysed by breaking the magnetic energy up into pairwise interactions.

The coupling constant J_1 strongly depends on the distance r_{ik} between atoms. For distances close to an atomic spacing the direct exchange interaction dominates. At the shortest interatomic distances r_{ws} the non-magnetic state (curve NM) is most stable, then the antiferromagnetic state (curve AF) takes over with increasing r_{ws}, and eventually the ferromagnetic state (curve HS) becomes favourable at the largest r_{ws}. Qualitative arguments are able to rationalise this behaviour: when highly compressed, electrons are forced into similar spatial wavefunctions with opposite spin to satisfy Pauli's exclusion principle. That reduces the magnetic moment and eliminates it altogether at the shortest distances.

The antiferromagnetic coupling at intermediate distances can be viewed as the exchange hole carried by an electron, which excludes parallel spins from its neighbourhood. At larger distances, electrons are able to reduce their Coulomb repulsion by occupying different spatial wavefunctions with equal spins. An indirect exchange interaction takes over at distances beyond a few atomic spacings. It is mediated by the s, p electrons. Spin i polarises the s, p-electron gas and a second spin k feels the induced polarisation. This interaction starts out ferromagnetic at small distances and oscillates with a period of $\lambda_F/2$, where $\lambda_F = 2\pi/k_F$ is the Fermi wavelength and k_F is the Fermi wave-vector.

The ferromagnetic coupling at small distances follows from a symmetry argument. Both spins interact in the same way with the s, p electrons, such that one has either a ↑↓↑ or a ↑↑↑ spin configuration. The oscillatory behaviour at larger distances arises because the s, p-electron gas responds to an extra spin by setting up a static spin wave. This wave contains spatial frequencies up to the wave-vector $2k_F$, which is the largest wave-vector of zeroenergy excitations across a spherical Fermi surface. In real space, the occupied states contain wavelengths from infinity down to λ_F. Charge and spin density are given by the square of the wavefunction, which oscillates with $\lambda_F/2$, twice as fast as the wavefunction itself. This indirect coupling via the s, p electrons is described to lowest order by the Ruderman-Kittel-Kasuya-Yosida (RKKY) interaction.

In order to obtain the magnetism of a bulk solid, one has to integrate over couplings between atom pairs in all directions and at many distances. Thus RKKY oscillations tend to become averaged out. In well defined layer structures, however, they remain visible and produce an oscillatory magnetic coupling. In the limit of retaining only nearest-neighbour terms, one arrives at the Heisenberg, the *xy* or the Ising model, depending on whether the magnetic moment vectors M have three, two or one degree of freedom. These are important for classifying magnetic phase transitions.

The ordinary bilinear coupling in equation (7a) exhibits either a minimum at 0° (J_1 positive; ferromagnetism) or at 180° (J_1 negative; antiferromagnetism) but cannot explain 90° coupling. The 90° coupling has been found in thin-film systems, such as Fe/Cr(100) when the film thickness is adjusted to the point where J_1 switches from ferromagnetic to antiferromagnetic. At distances larger than about 10 nm the magnetostatic dipole interaction takes over from the exchange coupling and orients particles or layers as if they were macroscopic bar magnets.

Magnetic anisotropy is another magnetic variable that becomes rather volatile as the bulk symmetry is reduced in small structures. In general, the magnetic energy density E varies quadratically with the angle ϑ of the magnetisation with respect to a symmetry axis in a crystal or film:

$$E = K\cos^2\vartheta. \tag{8}$$

The anisotropy constant K can be negative ('easy' axis) or positive ('hard' axis). If K vanishes by symmetry, such as in a cubic environment, fourth-order terms in ϑ take over. A variety of phenomena cause anisotropy, which may be grouped into crystalline and dipole anisotropy. The source of crystalline bulk anisotropy is the spin-orbit interaction. While atomic spin wavefunctions are isotropic by themselves, they become tied to the crystal lattice by spin-orbit interaction. Therefore the total magnetic moment (spin plus orbital moment) is coupled to the crystal axes.

For the common ferromagnetic materials the easy axes are [100] in bcc Fe, [0001] in hcp Co, [111] in fcc Ni, and [0001] in hcp Gd. In nanostructures the symmetry of the system is lowered by the existence of a surface or interface, where orbitals perpendicular and parallel to the interface become inequivalent. This symmetry breaking propels the anisotropy from a fourth-order effect to a second-order effect in Fe and Ni. Some surfaces exhibit an additional in-plane anisotropy, which can be intrinsic, for example for (110) surfaces of fcc and bcc structures, or step induced.

If there is lattice mismatch between a magnetic layer and the substrate, one encounters a magnetoelastic anisotropy which is related to magnetostriction. The second major source of anisotropy is the magnetic dipole interaction, which can be viewed as the energy density $-\frac{1}{2}M \cdot H_d$ of the magnetic moment M in the demagnetising field H_d. This shape anisotropy becomes important in thin films ($K_{dipole} = -2\pi M^2$) and for wires ($K_{dipole} = -\pi M^2$), where it aligns the magnetisation to the plane of a thin film or to the axis of a wire. For the analysis of the magnetic data in thin films, the bulk expression for magnetocrystalline anisotropy K_{bulk} has to be augmented by a thickness-dependent term $K_{interface}$ /d, which describes surface, interface and straininduced contributions to the magnetic energy density, averaged over the thickness of the film.

To this first approximation, the bulk terms are independent of thickness, while the surface and interface terms decrease in relative weight as the film becomes thicker. However, the bulk contribution is not necessarily independent of thickness either, since strain and alloying with the substrate may be thickness dependent. An example is the double transition from parallel to perpendicular and back to parallel, observed in Ni films on Cu(100) with increasing thickness. The Ni film is magnetised parallel to the surface up to seven atomic layers, driven by surface, interface and shape anisotropy. Between seven and about 40 monolayers, the magnetisation orients itself perpendicular, along the axis preferred by the strained Ni film.

A simple estimate of the relative strengths shows that with decreasing film thickness the interface anisotropy will eventually dominate, because its energy density scales like 1/d. This explains a frequently observed switch from parallel to perpendicular magnetisation in epitaxial films below about five monolayers coverage, for example in bcc Fe on Ag(100) and fcc Fe on Cu(100). Two-dimensional magnetism in thin films is dependent on the presence of anisotropy in a rather general fashion, because long-range magnetic ordering occurs only for the uniaxial Ising model, whereas an isotropic Heisenberg system cannot establish long-range order at finite temperatures.

8
Nanophotonic Structures

Nanophotonics deals with the interaction of light with
matter on a nanometer size scale. By adding a new
dimension to nanoscale science and technology,
nanophotonics provides challenges for fundamental
research and creates opportunities for new technologies.
The interest in nanoscience is a realization of a famous
statement by Feynman that "There's Plenty of Room at the
Bottom". He was pointing out that if one takes a length
scale of one micrometer and divides it in nanometer
segments, which are a billionth of a meter, one can imagine
how many segments and compartments become available to
manipulate. We are living in an age of "nano-mania."

Everything nano is considered to be exciting and
worthwhile. Many countries have started Nanotechnology
Initiatives. Nanophotonics can conceptually be divided into
three parts as shown in figure 1. One way to induce
interactions between light and matter on a nanometer size
scale is to confine light to nanoscale dimensions that are
much smaller than the wavelength of light.

The second approach is to confine matter to nanoscale
dimensions, thereby limiting interactions between light and
matter to nanoscopic dimensions. This defines the field of
nanomaterials. The last way is nanoscale confinement of a
photoprocess where we induce photochemistry or a light-
induced phase change. This approach provides methods for

nanofabrication of photonic structures and functional units. Let's look at nanoscale confinement of radiation. There are a number of ways in which one can confine the light to a nanometer size scale. One example is light squeezed through a metal-coated and tapered optical fiber where the light emanates through a tip opening that is much smaller than the wavelength of light. The nanoscale confinement of matter to make nanomaterials for photonics involves various ways of confining the dimensions of matter to produce nanostructures.

One can utilize nanoparticles that exhibit unique electronic and photonic properties. It is gratifying to find that these nanoparticles are already being used for various applications of nanophotonics such as UV absorbers in sunscreen lotions. Nanoparticles can be made of either inorganic or organic materials. Nanomers, which are nanometer size oligomers (a small number of repeat units) of monomeric organic structures, are organic analogues of nanoparticles.

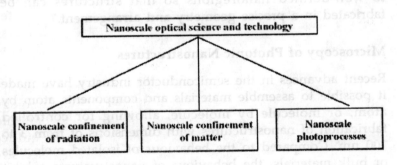

Figure 1. Nanophotonics

In contrast, polymers are long chain structures involving a large number of repeat units. These nanomers exhibit size-dependent optical properties. Metallic nanoparticles exhibit unique optical response and enhanced electromagnetic field and constitute the area of "plasmonics." Then there are nanoparticles which up-convert two absorbed IR photons into a photon in the visible UV range; conversely, there are nanoparticles, called quantum cutters, that down-convert an absorbed vacuum UV photon to two photons in the visible range. A hot area of nanomaterials is a photonic crystal that represents a periodic dielectric structure with a repeat unit of the order of wavelength of light. Nanocomposites comprise nanodomains of two or more dissimilar materials that are phase-separated on a nanometer size scale. Each nanodomain in the nanocomposite can impart a particular optical property to the bulk media.

Flow of optical energy by energy transfer (optical communications) between different domains can also be controlled. Nanoscale photoprocesses can be used for nanolithography to fabricate nanostructures. These nanostructures can be used to form nanoscale sensors and actuators. A nanoscale optical memory is one of exciting concepts of nanofabrication. An important feature of nanofabrication is that the photoprocesses can be confined to well-defined nanoregions so that structures can be fabricated in a precise geometry and arrangement.

Microscopy of Photonic Nanostructures

Recent advances in the semiconductor industry have made it possible to assemble materials and components atom by atom, or molecule by molecule, allowing for controlled fabrication of nanostructures with dimensions of from 3 to 100 nm. Compared to the behaviour of isolated molecules or bulk materials, the behaviour of nanostructures exhibit important physical properties not necessarily predictable from observations of either individual constituents or large ensembles. Predominant at the nanoscale are size confinement and quantum mechanical behaviour observed in optical and electronic properties, as well as distinct elastic and/or mechanical features-properties that have yet to be directly observed in many cases. Nano-optics addresses the broad spectrum of optics on the nanometre scale covering technology and basic science, spanning nanolithography to high-density optical data storage in technology, and from imaging individual quantum dots (QDs) to atom-photon interactions in the optical near-field in basic physical sciences.

Critical to any discussion of optical microscopy and spectroscopy are the fundamental limitations of conventional microscopy. In case of imaging objects with optical fields propagating in the far field, the basic constraint is the diffraction of light, which limits standard optical microscopy to a spatial resolution comparable to half the wavelength of light, as shown in Figure 2.

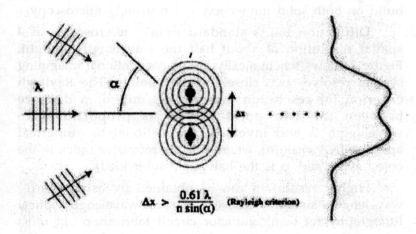

$$\Delta x > \frac{0.61\ \lambda}{n\ \sin(\alpha)} \quad \text{(Rayleigh criterion)}$$

Figure 2. Schematic representation of Rayleigh criterion showing the minimum detectable separation of two light scatterers for a given optical system

For imaging objects through a substrate, which is generally opaque for short wavelengths, this limitation becomes more stringent. Imaging guided-wave devices represents even a bigger challenge for conventional microscopy, since light does not couple to the far-field rendering conventional microscopy useless. Reducing the wavelength or increasing the collected solid angle can improve the spatial resolution of surface microscopy.

This has been achieved both with oil immersion and solid immersion lens (SIL) microscopy techniques, which reduce the wavelength by immersing the object space in a material with a high refractive index. The large in the object space in standard subsurface microscopy of planar samples does not increase the numerical aperture because of refraction at the planar boundary. Scientists have recently developed novel techniques based on a numerical aperture increasing lens (NAIL) to study semiconductors at very high spatial resolution. The techniques described below are build on both solid immersion and near-field microscopy.

Diffraction limits standard optical microscopy to a spatial resolution of about half the wavelength of light. Figure 2 shows schematically how a conventional imagining system resolves two closely spaced points. The Rayleigh criterion for resolution prescribes a minimum distance between the two point objects as proportional to wavelength λ and inversely proportional to numerical aperture [$NA = n\sin(\alpha)$, where n is the refractive index in the object space and α is the half-angle subtended].

Higher resolution can be obtained by using shorter wavelengths similar to the use of short-wavelength optical lithography for semiconductor circuit fabrication. In most microscopy and spectroscopy applications, however, the wavelength cannot be arbitrarily selected as it is determined by the optical properties of the materials under study. For example, optical absorption in silicon limits inspection through the substrate to $\lambda \geq 1\mu m$, yielding a theoretical lateral spatial resolution limit for standard subsurface microscopy of about 0.5 m.

In recent years, aperture microscopy technique called near-field optical microscopy (NSOM) has extended the range of optical measurements beyond the diffraction limit and stimulated interests in many disciplines, especially material and biological sciences. Aperture scanning near-field microscopy, first described in the early years of the 1900s, is a technique that allows for arbitrarily small details to be resolved by scanning a small aperture over the object. Light can only pass through the aperture, and so the aperture size and its proximity to the object determine the resolution of the system, as shown in Figure 3.

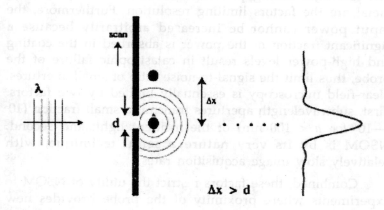

Figure 3. Schematic of aperture scanning near-field microscopy.

Near-field optical techniques can be applied to probe complex semiconductor nanostructures as well as individual molecules. Recent NSOM studies of materials and devices have addressed issues of laser diode mode profiling, minority carrier transport, near-field photocurrent response of quantum-well structures and laser diodes, imaging of local waveguide properties, and location and studies of dislocations in semiconductor thin films. NSOM studies of nanostructures have revealed novel optical properties of coupled quantum cubes, and self-assembled QDs, the super-resolution providing the necessary spatial discrimination. Work on photonic bandgap systems has also continued, striving to image the localised photon states in the bandgap resonance. Studies have also focused on artificial nanostructures, elucidating the plasmon properties of noble metal particles and waveguides, and polymer nanoparticles. In the most widely adopted aperture approach, light is sent down an aluminum-coated tapered fiber tip of which the foremost end is left uncoated to form a small aperture.

Unfortunately, most NSOM probes created by heating and pulling have transmissions of ~10^{-4} due to mode cutoff. The low light throughput and the finite skin depth of the metal are the factors limiting resolution. Furthermore, the input power cannot be increased arbitrarily because a significant fraction of the power is absorbed in the coating and high-power levels result in catastrophic failure of the probe, thus limit the signal-to-noise ratio of small apertures. Near-field microscopy is essentially limited by two factors. First, subwavelength apertures transmit a small fraction (10^{-4}—10^{-6} for $a < 100$ nm) of the incident light; and second, NSOM is by its very nature a serial technique, with relatively slow image acquisition rates.

Combined, these factors restrict the utility of NSOM to experiments where proximity of the probe provides new information and where the source is bright, largely time independent and long lived. As a result, time resolved, pump probe, Raman, and nonlinear spectroscopies are not widespread.

Solid Immersion Lens Microscopy (SIL) improves resolution without the huge loss of light associated with NSOM through the use of a semispherical lens of high index. For some applications such as quantum-dot characterisation, the SIL can significantly improve the light collection efficiency beyond that of conventional optical microscopy. This makes it especially attractive for spectroscopy of quantum structures, where both high resolution and large light collection efficiency are requirements. In addition, when the semisphere is index matched to a substrate material, SIL microscopy provides special imaging capabilities for subsurface microscopy. The SIL is a solid plano-convex lens of high refractive index that provides an optimum focus of a Gaussian beam.

There are two configurations with a semispherical lens that achieve diffraction-limited performance. One focus exists at the centre of the sphere, with incoming rays perpendicular to the surface and is generally termed an SIL. Also, a second focus exists at a set of aplanatic points R/n a distance below the centre of the sphere, and whose rays are refracted at the spherical surface. This type is generally referred to as a super-SIL, or Weierstrass optic. While the super-SIL configuration has a greater magnification (n^2 versus n) and increased numerical aperture, it suffers from strong chromatic aberration.

The applications of solid immersion microscopy fall into two categories: surface and subsurface imaging. In the latter, the SIL (or super-SIL) is used to image objects below the lens and into the sample under study. In this case of subsurface imaging, a good match in index between the lens and substrate must be maintained. SIL microscopy was originally envisioned for optical data storage, but has recently seen several important physics and nanoimaging, applications. Solid immersion lenses exploit the existence of a significant amount of light above the critical angle for the high resolution and large collection efficiency.

This leads to a unique aspect of surface SIM: When the optical index of the investigated object is smaller than that of the lens material, as is usually the case of most materials, then the plane wave components of the focused wave undergo total internal reflection when impinging the SIL/object interface above critical angle. Total internal reflection (TIR) produces local evanescent waves in the vicinity of the focal point, an aspect that is often put forward in the literature as extending SIM to near-field optical microscopy. However, TIR is also accompanied with an inseparable combination of more subtle phenomena which stem from the slower wave propagation velocity in the SIL material. In solid-state systems, this is referred to as the Goos-Hänchen reflected beam displacement and has an analogy in geological sciences called v. Schmidt's lateral waves. In the Goos-Hänchen effect, the photons that are tunneling into the less optically dense object medium reemerge into the SIL laterally displaced from impinging point.

This produces a lateral beam shift of the total internal reflected plane wave components. The v. Schmidt's lateral waves, well known in seismology, trails the diverging reflected wave components originating from the focused spot in the form of a conical wave front in a way similar to the Mach cone in fluid dynamics. Such TIR-related effects lead to a sizable aberration in the image formation of the focused spot. Luckily this aberration does not affect the actual size of the probing focused spot. Furthermore, it can be used in conjunction with confocal microscopy in order to greatly enhance the reflected image contrast of lowoptical index objects.

Figure 4 displays a comparison of theory and experiment of the image of a tightly focused spot at the interface between a high-index SIL and a low-index medium. The results of both indicate that a significant fraction of optical power reflected from the interface is laterally displaced; thus, a confocal arrangement yields higher than expected contrast with lower than expected reflected power. Similarly, the probing spot as defined by the incident waves is tightly focused, as expected. When imaging below the planar surface of a sample, refraction prevents a conventional optical microscope from operating with a resolution near the diffraction limit. The spatial resolution is not improved by the larger index of the material because light cannot be externally coupled beyond the critical angle. By adding a lens to the backside planar surface of the sample this light can be externally coupled, yielding improved resolution and larger collection efficiency.

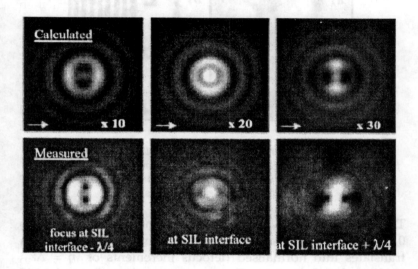

Figure 4. Comparison of experiment and theory demonstrating the aberrations due to the Goos–Hänchen reflected beam displacement.

The imaging quality is greatly improved over that of the surface SIL, because the interface is out of focus. This is the second, subsurface configuration referred to above. Here we have demonstrated the improvement in resolution that the lens provides by inspection of silicon integrated circuits through the substrate.

Though the lateral spatial resolution can be evaluated from a lateral intensity distribution, the dielectric interfaces in the vertical, or longitudinal direction, create a complicated transfer function that does not facilitate a simple evaluation of the longitudinal spatial resolution. By measuring the modulation transfer function (MTF)-the ratio of object to image contrast-of a laterally periodic structure with longitudinal defocusing, we can test the longitudinal spatial resolution.

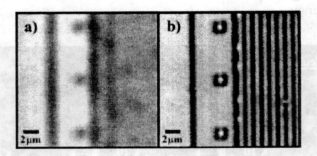

Figure 5. (a) Lateral line scans of a periodic structure with a spatial frequency of s=0.4 μm1. (b) Measured values and theoretical function of the modulation transfer function plotted by normalised defocus values.

The resulting normalised spatial frequency $v = s \cdot \lambda_0/NA = 0.3$. Defocusing the sample by Δz increments of 1μm translates into normalised defocus increments of $\eta = \Delta z \cdot NA^2/ 2 \cdot \lambda_0/ \cdot n. = 0.33$. The experimentally measured MTF values are compared to the MTF function the optical system would exhibit if it were diffraction limited in Figure 7. The decay in coupling of this spatial frequency indicates the system is close to diffraction limited. With the 5X microscope objective lens and NAIL we have ~1.3 μm longitudinal spatial resolution, whereas a 100 microscope objective lens has ~12 μm longitudinal spatial resolution. The spatial resolution improvement laterally is at least a factor of 3.5 while longitudinally it is at least a factor of 12.5. The greatest longitudinal resolution is 280 nm, which would allow vertical sectioning of an integrated circuit's layer structure.

QDs have received an enormous amount of interest in recent years because they serve as an excellent new system to study basic quantum physics with engineered atomic-like properties. Coherence, coupling, carrier dynamics and other fundamental properties are only accessible when individual dots are examined experimentally.

For a self-assembled QD sample, the typical QD size is ~20 nm and areal QD density is 10^8~10^{10}/cm^2. So to excite just a few dots within a small spectral window, the sample area under investigation must be reduced to a few hundred nanometers in size. To accomplish this, one approach is aperturing or focusing the excitation laser tightly to a spot size of that magnitude.

Another approach is creating a mask or etching a mesa on the sample itself. The latter technique has the major drawback that spatial scanning and spectral imaging cannot be performed and, thus, the interactions between neighbouring dots, diffusion, wave function spatial structure, and other optical properties cannot be investigated.

Near-field scanning optical microscopy (NSOM) has been used to probe a small number of QDs. Saiki's group used NSOM to investigate the homogeneous linewidth broadening of single InGaAs QD at room temperature with a spatial resolution of 250 nm, which is determined by the aperture diameter of NSOM tip. For the past five years, many groups has used NSOM to investigate the physics of self-assembled QDs (SADs) at low temperature. The resolution provided by NSOM allows the interrogation of individual QDs, even in the density regime where dot-to-dot coupling occurs.

The throughput of NSOM is low and cryogenic NSOM experiments complex. Solid immersion microscopic techniques have been developed to overcome these limitations of NSOM but still provide similar ultrahigh spatial resolution. Grober's group has implemented solid immersion lens in imaging spectroscopy of quantum well and QDs, achieving a spatial resolution of 240 nm. Many groups are utilising backside immersion microscopy and scanning confocal microscopy to investigate the physics of InGaAs QDs, especially the dynamics of excitons in QDs, decoherence, and coupling between QDs.

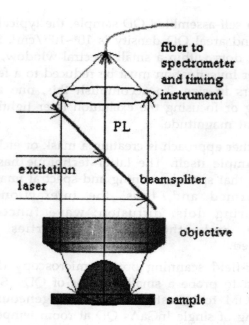

Figure 6. Schematic of confocal microscope combined with solid immersion NAIL technique.

The numeric aperture of the system is increased by $\sim n^2 = 13$ achieving a spatial resolution of ~120 nm. Due to the high NA of systems, collection efficiency will be large enough to perform time resolved PL experiments as well pump-probe experiments on individual dots without resorting to aperture, mask, or etched mesa techniques.

Tip-enhanced Near-field Optical Microscopy

In aperture-type near-field optical microscopy, light is sent down an aluminum-coated fiber tip of which the foremost end is left uncoated to form a small aperture. Unfortunately, only a tiny fraction of the light coupled into the fiber is emitted through the aperture because of the cutoff of propagation of the waveguide modes.

The low light throughput and the finite skin depth of the metal are the limiting factors for resolution. Nowadays, it is doubted that an artifact-free resolution of 50 nm will be surpassed by the aperture technique. However, many applications in nanotechnology require higher spatial resolutions. Recently, a new apertureless technique has been introduced to overcome the limitations of aperture probes. The technique makes use of the strongly enhanced electric field close to a sharply pointed metal tip under laser illumination.

The energy density close to the metal tip can be strongly increased over the energy density of the illuminating laser light. The tip is held a few nanometers above the sample surface so that a highly localised interaction between the enhanced field and the sample is achieved. In order to obtain a high image contrast, nonlinear optical interactions based on multiphoton processes have been used. With this technique, spectroscopic measurements with spatial optical resolutions on the order of 10 nm have been achieved. To date, this is the highest reported spatial resolution of a spectroscopic measurement. The use of laser-illuminated metal tips for near-field imaging has been discussed by many groups but most of the work has been limited to light scattering at the metal tip.

The tip locally perturbs the fields at the sample surface; the response to this perturbation is detected in the far-field at the same frequency of the incident light. Homodyne detection using lock-in techniques is commonly applied to discriminate the signal against the background.

Interference with a reference field has been introduced to increase the contrast and it has been demonstrated that more specific information can be extracted by detecting the scattering signal at higher harmonics of the vibration frequency. In general, the detected signals contain both near-field and far-field contributions, and often are dominated by topographic rather than spectroscopic information. The interpretation of the contrast in the recorded images is therefore difficult.

Instead of using the metal tip as a local scatterer, it can also be used as a local light source if proper polarisation and excitation conditions are met. The field near the tip apex can become strongly enhanced over the field of the illuminating laser light thereby establishing a nanoscopic light-source. Thus, instead of using a tip to locally scatter the sample's near-field, the tip is used to provide a local excitation source for a spectroscopic response of the sample. This approach enables simultaneous spectral and subdiffraction spatial measurements, but it depends sensitively on the magnitude of the field enhancement factor. The latter is a function of wavelength, material, geometry, and polarisation of the exciting light field. Although theoretical investigations have led to a wide range of values for the field enhancement factor these studies are consistent with respect to polarisation conditions and local field distributions.

In Figure 7(a), the tip is irradiated from the bottom by an on-axis fundamental Gaussian beam for which the polarisation is perpendicular to the tip axis. On the other hand, in Figure 7 (c) the tip is irradiated by a focused, on-axis Hermite-Gaussian (1,0) mode which possesses a strong longitudinal field at the center of its focus. Figure 7(b) and (d) show corresponding cuts along a transverse line 1 nm beneath the tip. A striking difference is seen for the two different excitations: in Figure 7 (c) , the intensity near the tip end is strongly increased over the illuminating intensity, whereas no enhancement beneath the tip exists in Figure 7(a). This result suggests that it is crucial to have a large component of the excitation field along the axial direction to obtain a high field enhancement.

Calculations of platinum and tungsten tips show lower enhancements, whereas the field beneath a dielectric tip is

reduced compared to the excitation field. The incident light
drives the free electrons in the metal along the direction of
polarisation. While the charge density is zero inside the
metal at any instant of time (div E = 0), charges accumulate
on the surface of the metal. When the incident polarisation
is perpendicular to the tip axis, diametrically opposed
points on the tip surface have opposite charges. As a
consequence, the foremost end of the tip remains
uncharged.

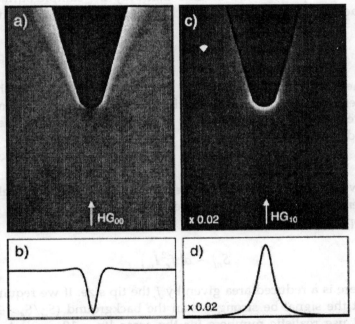

*Figure 7. Calculated near-field of a gold tip (5-nm tip radius)
irradiated at* λ = 810 nm *with two different focused laser modes along
the tip axis. (a), (b) Gaussian laser mode, and (c), (d) Hermite–
Gaussian (1,0) mode. (a), (c) show plots of the electric field intensity
(E^2) and (b), (d) are linecuts of (a), (c) evaluated on a transverse line 1
nm beneath the tip.*

On the other hand, when the incident polarisation is parallel
to the tip axis, the induced surface charge density is

rotationally symmetric and has the highest amplitude at the end of the tip. In both cases, the surface charges form an oscillating standingwave with wavelengths shorter than thewavelength of illuminating light indicating that it is essential to include retardation in the analysis. The magnitude of the field enhancement factor is crucial for imaging applications. The direct illumination of the sample surface gives rise to a far-field background signal. If we consider an optical interaction that is based on a nth-order nonlinear process and assume that only the sample surface is active, then the far-field background will be proportional to

$$S_{ff} \sim A I_o^n$$

where is the illuminated surface area and is the laser intensity. The signal that we wish to detect and investigate (near-field signal) is excited by the enhanced field at the tip.

If we designate the enhancement factor for the electric field intensity (E) by f_e then the near-field signal of interest is proportional to

$$S_{nf} \sim a \left(f_e^2 I_o \right)^n$$

where is a reduced area given by f_e the tip size. If we require that the signal be stronger than the background ($S_{nf}/S_{ff} > 1$) and use realistic numbers for the areas [($a = 10$ nm)^2, A = (500 nm)^2] then we find that an enhancement factor of

$$f_e > \left[2500\right]^{1/2n}$$

is required. For a first-order process ($n = 1$) such as scattering or fluorescence, an enhancement factor of 50 is required which is beyond the calculated values. Therefore, it is necessary to involve higher order nonlinear processes.

For a second-order nonlinear process, the required enhancement factor is only 7. This is the reason why the first experiments have been performed with two-photon excitation.

To maximise the field enhancement, various alternative probe shapes and materials have been proposed. It has been determined that finite-sized elongated shapes exhibit very low radiation damping and, therefore, provide very high enhancement factors. Even stronger enhancements are found for tetrahedral shapes. In fluorescence studies, the enhanced field is used to locally excite the sample under investigation to a higher electronic state or band.

Image formation is based on the subsequent fluorescence emission. However, the fluorescence can be quenched by the presence of the probe, i.e., the excitation energy can be transferred to the probe and be dissipated through various channels into heat.

Thus, there is a competition between field enhancement and fluorescence quenching. The nonradiative energy transfer rate from molecule to the tip depends on the inverse sixth power of the distance d between tip and molecule, similar to the case of Förster energy transfer.

However, the excitation rate of the molecule also depends on d^{-6}, since it is proportional to the square of the electric near-field. Hence, for small distances from the tip, there should be no distance dependence of the fluorescence rate of a single molecule if excited by a single photon. Of course, this is a rough estimate and more accurate calculations are needed to understand the interplay between field enhancement and quenching. While quenching is an issue in fluorescence imaging, there are various applications in near-field optics that are not sensitive to such a competing process.

We believe that the combination of field enhancement and nonlinear optical interactions is very promising for technological applications, such as semiconductor mask inspection and lithography. In the past, it has been proposed to perform nanolithography with the sharp tip of an atomic force microscope.

However, this is an intrusive technique since it is based on a mechanical interaction between probe and sample. The optical tip-enhanced technique should be able to achieve comparable resolution, and since it is based on an optical interaction, it does not require a physical contact between probe and sample.

Since the optical writing in most photoresists is based on nonlinear processes, the prerequisites for this technique are readily met. Furthermore, the technique benefits strongly from the existing knowledge of conventional optical lithography. Optical data storage based on a solid immersion lens (SIL) has proven to be a fast technique since it does not rely on piezo-positioning. Instead, a constant tip-sample distance is maintained by the air cushion formed between the end-face of the SIL and the rotating sample surface.

In the past, many scientists have analysed the focusing capabilities of SILs and determined the polarisation properties. To understand the effect of local field enhancement in combination with SIL, a recent study carried out rigorous calculations based on Maxwell's equations using the MMP method.

A radially polarised laser beam is focused on the interface of an optical element with a flat surface. A tip-shaped aluminum particle is placed in close proximity to the surface of the optical element. The end diameter of the tip-shaped particle is 10 nm and the distance to the surface of the optical element is 5 nm. The incoming radially polarised laser light has a wavelength of 800 nm. The figure shows contour lines of constant electric field intensity on a logarithmic scale.

The linecuts below Figure 7c represent the electric field intensity 1 nm above the surface of the optical element for the case with and without the tip-shaped particle. This figure demonstrates the much smaller spotsise that can be achieved by using a small structure to enhance the fields. In this particular example, the optical data density can be increased by roughly a factor of 900.

The metal tip is replaced by a favourably shaped particle located close to the SIL's planar surface and irradiated by a radially polarised laser beam which provides the necessary polarisation conditions. The TESIL is built using conventional silicon microfabrication.

First, SIL lenses are bonded on the back surface of a 100-mm silicon wafer, and a thin layer of resist is deposited on the front surface of the wafer. A small hole (or holes) is made in the resist by an electron or ion beam. After metal deposition and removal of the resist, the small resulting metal particle is protected by a silicon nitride coating.The concept extends to parallel imaging. With a grid of particles of separation greater than half a wavelength, conventional beam-steering methods could be used to address the particles one at a time, or multiple beams could be used for faster read/write.

Development in Nanophotonics

We live in a complex world where revolutionary progress has been and continues to be made in communications, computer memory, and data processing. There is a growing need for new technologies that rapidly detect and treat diseases at an early stage or even pre-stage. As we get accustomed to these advances, our expectations will demand more compact, energy-efficient, rapidly responding, and environmentally safe technologies. Photonic-based technology, coupled with nanotechnology, can meet many of these challenges.

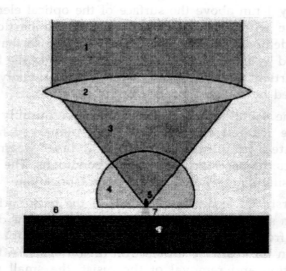

*Figure 8. Combination of SIL with local field enhancement. (1)
Incoming laser light with a mode profile that provides an electric field
in its focal region perpendicular to the surface of the optical element,
(2) focusing lens, (3) focused laser light, (4) optical element, (5) small
structure able to locally enhance the electric field of the incoming laser
light, (6) sample surface to be optically interacted with, and (7)
localised optical interaction.*

In the medical area, new modes of photonic diagnostics,
which are noninvasive and molecular-based, may recognize
the prestages and onset of a disease such as cancer and thus
provide a major leap. Nanomedicine, combined with light-
guided and activated therapy, will advance individualized
therapy that is based on molecular recognition and thus
have minimal side effects.

The past several decades have witnessed major
technological breakthroughs produced by fusion of different
disciplines. This trend is even more likely in this millenium.
Nanophotonics in its broader vision offers opportunities for
interactions among many traditionally disparate disciplines

of science, technology, and medicine. As shall be illustrated in this book, nanophotonics is an interdisciplinary field that comprises physics, chemistry, applied sciences and engineering, biology, and biomedical technology.

A significant multidisciplinary challenge lies ahead for the broader nanophotonics visions to become reality. These challenges require a significant increase in the number of knowledgeable researchers and trained personnel in this field. This need can be met by providing a multidisciplinary training for a future generation of researchers at both undergraduate and graduate levels, worldwide. A worldwide recognition of this vital need is evident from the growing number of conferences and workshops being held on this topic, as well as from the education and training programs being offered or contemplated at various institutions.

Some have considered near-field interactions and near-field microscopy as the major thrust of nanophotonics, while others have considered it to be focused in photonic crystals. Another major direction has been nanomaterials, particularly the ones exhibiting size dependence of their optical properties; these are the quantum-confined structures. For engineers, nanoscale optical devices and nanolithography are the most relevant aspects of nanophotonics.

In terms of optical materials, the scientific community is often divided in two traditional groups: inorganic and organic, with very little cross-fertilization. The physics community focuses on inorganic semiconductors and metals, while shying away from complex organic structures.

The chemical community, on the other hand, deals traditionally with organic structures and biomaterials and feels less comfortable with inorganic semiconductors, particularly with concepts defining their electronic and optical properties. Importantly, a new generation of hybrid nanomaterials, which involve different levels of integration of organic and inorganic structures, holds considerable promise for new fundamental science and novel technologies. For example, novel chemical routes can be utilized to prepare inorganic semiconductor nanostructures for nanophotonics.

Engineers, who could exploit these new materials' flexibility for fabrication of components with diverse functionalities and their heterogeneous integration, often lack experience in dealing with these materials. Biologists have a great deal to offer by providing biomaterials for nanophotonics.

At the same time, biological and biomedical researchers can utilize nanophotonics to study cellular processes and use nano-optical probes for diagnosis and to effect light-guided and activated therapy.

Often, a major hurdle is the lack of a common language to foster effective communication across disciplines. Therefore, much is to be gained by creating an environment that includes these disciplines and facilitates their interactions. This book will address all these issues. It proposes to fill the existing void by providing the following features:

— A unifying, multifaceted description of nanophotonics that includes near-field interactions, nanomaterials, photonic crystals, and nanofabrication

— A focus on nanoscale optical interactions, nanostructured optical materials and applications of nanophotonics

— A coverage of inorganic, organic materials, and biomaterials as well as their hybrids

— A broad view of nanolithography for nanofabrication

— A coverage of nanophotonics for biomedical research and nanomedicine

— A critical assessment of nanophotonics in the market place, with future forecasts.

9
Carbon Nanowalls

The discovery of fullerenes and carbon nanotubes, a great deal of effort has been devoted to the development of similar types of nanostructures made up of other materials such as WS_2, MoS_2, NbS_2, BN, BC_2N, BC_3, $NiCl_2$, and CN, etc. The common feature of these materials is that they have a layered structure in the bulk form. When the size of these materials in one direction decreases to a few or tens of monolayers, the material becomes a thin sheet which is usually unstable and tends to curve and roll up in either one or more directions; this will lead to the formation of various types of nanostructures such as fullerenes, cages, cones, and tubes. The unique shape and symmetry of these nanostructures give rise to unique mechanical, electronic, magnetic, and optoelectronic properties which their bulk counterparts lack.

Take the carbon nanotube as an example: it can be either a metal or a semiconductor, depending on the direction along which the graphene sheet is rolled up to form the tubular structure. This makes the nanotubes very attractive for future applications in electronics, optoelectronics, and sensors.

The large strength of the nanotubes also makes them an ideal building block for nanomechanical devices. In contrast to the closed boundary structure of the fullerenes and nanotubes, the 2D graphite sheets are characterised by an open boundary. Theoretical studies have shown that this may bring about nanocarbons' unique transport and magnetic properties. Of particular interest is the theoretical predication of ferromagnetism and superconducting instability in 2D graphite sheets and possible existence of unique transport properties.

In addition, the 2D nano-sheets also have a surface area which is theoretically twice that of the closed boundary structures, making them more attractive for chemical and biosensor applications. The sharp edges are also promising for field-emission applications. In spite of the unique properties of 2D nanocarbons predicted by theory, they are yet to be verified experimentally. This is mainly due to the unavailability of such kinds of samples.

One of the possible reasons is that nanometer-sized 2D carbons are not stable and tend to form tubular or cage structures. Recently they succeeded in the growth of well-aligned 2D carbons (dubbed carbon nanowalls) on various substrates using microwave plasma enhanced chemical vapour deposition (MPECVD). The 2D carbons form a self-supported network structure which enhances their stability.

Fig. 1(a) shows a typical SEM image of the carbon nanowalls. The distribution of the nanowalls is remarkably uniform over the whole substrate surface area that is typically 1 cm × 1 cm. Fig. 1(b) shows some of the nanowalls peeled off from the substrate and laid down on top of the nanowall samples. The nanowalls grow very fast within the first 1-2 minutes and nearly stop growing after they reach a height of about 2 μm. The width is in the range of 0.1-2 μm; it increases with decreasing the nanowall density.

The thickness of the nanowalls is typically in the range of one to several nanometers, as shown by the HRTEM images in Fig. 1(c) and (d). Note that the HRTEM image at the center portion of Fig. 1(c) was taken from a pile of carbon nano-sheets. The thickness of the nanowall can be estimated from the HRTEM image of a single piece of nano-sheet, as indicated by the arrow in the top right-hand corner of Fig. 1(c).

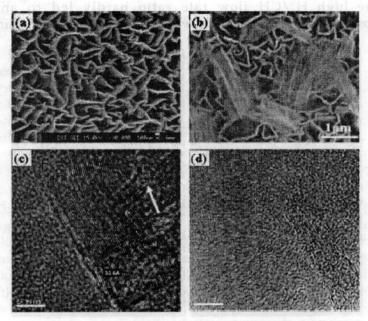

Figure 1. [(a) and (b)] SEM and [(c) and (d)] HRTEM images of carbon nanowalls.

Both the SEM and HRTEM observations show that there are two different types of nanowalls, one an open boundary nanographite sheet [Fig. 2(c)], and the other one more like a flattened tube with an empty interior [Fig. 1(d)]; the former predominates.

Gas Flow

The hydrogen-to-methane flow rate ratio was found to cause rather drastic changes to the morphology of the nanocarbon films. Fig. 2 shows the morphology of the carbon films grown on Au (ca. 20 nm) coated Si substrates at different H_2/CH_4 flow rate ratios. The growth pressure was 1 Torr. MPECVD is a well-known technique for growing diamond films at a H_2/CH_4 flow rate ratio of 100. As the growth temperature in this work is about 650-700°C, the high H_2/CH_4 flow rate ratio hardly led to any observable growth of carbon within a short period of 5 min.

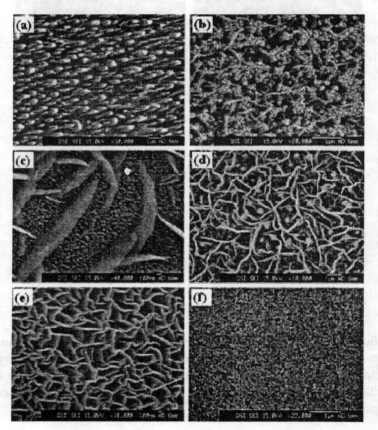

Figure 2. SEM images of carbon grown at different H_2/CH_4 flow rate ratios: (a) 30, (b) 15, (c) 10, (d) 6, (e) 4, (f) 1.

As the flow rate ratio is decreased to 30, some columnar structure of amorphous carbon forms. A further decrease of the gas flow rate ratio leads to the formation of a mixture of fibers/tubes and 2D nanographite sheets. A pure form of carbon nanowalls forms when the gas flow rate ratio is in the range of 4-8. The amorphous carbon forms again when the ratio is too low.

Influence of Electrical Field

In the early stages of the work on carbon nanowalls, the researchers found that the key to growing the nanowalls instead of nanotubes was the emergence of a strong lateral field caused by the nonuniform charging of the catalyst islands. However, in subsequent experiments, it was found that the nanowalls could also grow on substrates without any catalysts. This seemed to cast some doubt on the initial findings and prompted them to perform more experiments under a controlled environment for investigation of the electric field influence.

In order to find unambiguous evidence on the effect of the electrical field, they performed the following: (i) to use surface plasmons (SPs) to excite localised electrical field, (ii) to use large metal droplets as the catalysts, and (iii) to create sharp features on the substrate surface. The surface plasmon was known to cause large enhancement of local electrical fieldsand thus it was expected that the presence of a localised surface plasmon would affect the growth of carbon nanowalls locally.

As expected, the influence of the surface plasmon on the growth of carbon nanowalls was a rather drastic one. The circular region consists of an outer ring with denser nanowalls and a flower-like nanowall structure at the center. The latter consists of one to several poles and the number of poles increases with the density of the nanowalls surrounding the circular region, so is the size of the whole region. However, the occupation ratio of the outer ring in the whole circular region decreases when the number of poles increases. For clarity, the sample was tilted by 20°

when taking this picture. It shows clearly that the nanowalls orient randomly outside the circular region, while they align well along the circumference direction in the rim region and change the direction by almost 90° when they move further to the central region.

It demonstrates clearly how the carbon nanowalls change their orientation in an extremely localised region. This could hardly be possible without the existence of strongly localised electric fields induced by the surface plasmon. The patterns shown in panels (a)-(h) resemble well the electric field distribution of multiple pole SP predicted by Mie's theory with the number of poles increasing from (a) to (h). It is interesting to note that patterns with both odd and even numbers of poles were observed, though Mie's theory for a metallic sphere only predicts patterns with an even number of poles. This was probably caused by the uneven shape of the Au particles, which has been confirmed by the SEM observation of Au particles formed on bare substrates.

The size of the pattern increases with the number of poles: it is ca. 8 μm for the dipole pattern shown in panel (a) and 20 μm for the multiple pole patterns shown in (g) and (h). Assuming that the surface plasmon emission travels at the same speed of light in vacuum, it gives lifetimes of ca. 25 and 70fs, respectively.

These values agree well with the reported lifetimes for surface plasmons reported in the literature. Although the theory for calculating the electrical field distribution of SPs has existed for about a century since the pioneering work of Mie, it has been difficult to observe the field distribution experimentally due to the strong localisation and short lifetime of such fields. In addition to gaining an insight into the growth mechanism of the carbon nanowalls, this work has also successfully 'fingerprinted' the electric field of the SP at nanometer-scale accuracy. This is a remarkable result because it is the only technique reported so far which can detect the electrical field instead of the intensity of the SPs. The effect of the electrical field can also be seen clearly in the region where the two surface plasmons interfere constructively. The interaction occurs through the coherent addition of the electric fields of the two SPs. As a result, the electric field distribution of both SPs inside the interaction region was mutually perturbed, while that of the larger SP outside the interaction region remains almost intact.

Fig. 3 shows one such example in which a smaller plasmon (B) is contained within a larger plasmon (A). In the case of an isolated SP, the nanowalls just next to the rim region are oriented in the radial direction of the circular pattern. This is still true along line BE in Fig. 3 where the radial directions of the two circular patterns coincide.

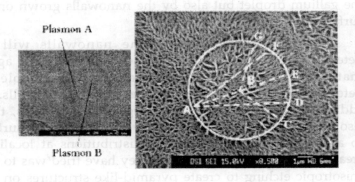

Figure 3. SEM image of the carbon nanowalls grown in the area where two surface plasmons interfere constructively.

On the other hand, at the cross point of AD and BC, and AF and BG, the nanowalls are oriented in the direction which almost bisects the two radial directions. This implies that the nanowalls are orientated in the total electrical field direction which is the vector sum of the electrical fields from the two SPs. In the above experiment, they used Au nanoparticles to excite surface plasmons which in turn generate localised fields to alter the growth of carbon nanowalls. Another natural way to create localised field distributions is to put large metallic particles on the substrate surface which would generate unique field distributions surrounding the particles. They chosen gallium for the metallic particles because of its low meting point.

However, once the surface stress becomes too high due to the temperature rise or weakening of the surface tension due to the incorporation of carbon into the surface layer, the large gallium droplets break from the top to form disk-like shapes like the ones shown in panels (b) and (e). In this case, the orientation of the nanowalls changes from the radial direction in the proximity of the droplet surface to the circumference direction next to it and then finally back to the radial direction. It seems that the dynamic field distribution is not only determined by the topography of the gallium droplet but also by the nanowalls grown on its surfaces.

The final orientation of the nanowalls will be determined self-consistently. These results suggest again that the electrical field plays an important role in determining the orientation of the carbon nanowalls. In addition to the use of SPs and large metal droplets, they also tried to modify the morphology of the substrate surface so as to alter the electrical field distributions at localised areas. One of the approaches that they have tried was to use anisotropic etching to create pyramid-like structures on the Si substrate.

Owing to the sharp features of the pyramids, the electrical field was expected to be enhanced at the locations of the pyramids which would thus affect the growth of the carbon nanowalls. As shown in Fig. 4(b)-(d), the size of the nanowalls grown on top of the pyramids is apparently larger than that of the nanowalls formed in other places. The directionality of the nanowalls grown on top of the pyramids was also improved as compared with those grown in the flat surface regions.

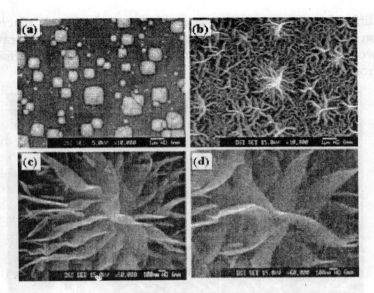

Figure 4. SEM images of (a) pyramid structures formed on a Si substrate using anisotropic etching, and (b)–(d) carbon nanowalls grown on the Si substrate with the pyramid structures.

Growth mechanism

The electrical field comes from both the DC bias and the nonuniform charging up of the substrate; the latter can be altered by the existence of metallic particles and other types of sharp features. When the metallic particles act as both a catalyst and a field modulator, both nanotubes and nanowalls can be formed depending on the strength of the lateral electrical field and other growth parameters such as the gas flow rate, temperature, and pressure.

However, when non-catalytic particles or bare substrates are used, it is more likely that carbon nanowalls will be formed. To shed some light on how the nanowall was formed, Fig. 5 shows the SEM images of the nanowalls at different growth stages on the Si substrate coated with a 20-nm-thick gold layer. The images were taken from different portions of the same substrate which was placed on the substrate holder in such a way that the growth rate would vary from one side to the other due to the offset from the optimum position.

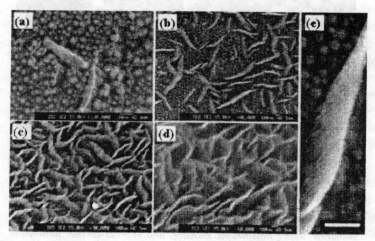

Figure 5. SEM images of carbon nanowalls grown on a Si substrate at different stages of growth using Au as the catalyst.

During the pre-heating stage, the Au film becomes isolated nanoparticles. At the very beginning of the growth, carbon forms surrounding the Au particles; but instead of forming a closed tubular structure, they expanded in the lateral directions and finally became connected with one another to form larger walllike structures. As shown in panel (e), at the initial stage, the walls are not single pieces of graphite but are made up of individual half-opened tubules. With the progress of the growth, the individual half-opened tubules expand in the lateral direction to form single pieces of nanowalls.

Properties of Carbon Nanowalls

The unique morphology and geometric shape of the nanowalls make them promising for field-emission applications. To this end, a series of experiments have been carried out to investigate the field-emission characteristics of the nanowalls. The nanowalls for the field-emission experiments were grown on 1 cm × 1 cm Cu substrates. The field-emission measurements were carried out in a vacuum chamber at a base pressure of 1×10^{-5} Torr. A polished copper (1 cm × 1 cm) anode was positioned 20-200 μm away from the nanowall cathode to collect the emitted electrons from the latter. As the base pressure of the measurement chamber is relatively high, the measurements were carried out at different temperatures so as to investigate the effect of absorbates on the nanowall surfaces.

The turn-on electrical field usually increases with decreasing the anode-cathode distance. It is typically in the range of 1-1.5 V μm⁻¹ at an emission current density of 10 μA cm⁻², though the value can be much smaller for some 'best case' samples. Fig. 6 shows the emission current densities as a function of the applied electric field for one of such samples obtained at temperatures of 20, 200, 300 and 400°C, and at an anode-cathode distance of 50 μm. The experiments were carried at 20°C first, and then repeated at different temperatures after the substrate was heated up using a resistive heater and stabilised at each temperature setting point.

The current densities were 0.19 and 9.53 mA cm⁻² at electrical fields of 0.32 and 0.62 V μm⁻, respectively. The turn-on electric field decreased to 0.26, 0.2 and 0.16 V/μm with the temperature increasing to 200, 300 and 400°C, respectively. The highest emission current density obtained was 17.6 mA cm⁻² at an applied electric field of 0.32 V μm⁻¹ at 400°C. A further increase of the applied electric field resulted in arcing, which prevented them from evaluating the highest possible current density. This is in part caused by the high base pressure of the particular measurement chamber. Fig. 6(b) shows the corresponding Fowler-Nordheim (F-N) plots of the field-emission curves shown in Fig. 6(a).

applications. To this end, a series of experiments have been

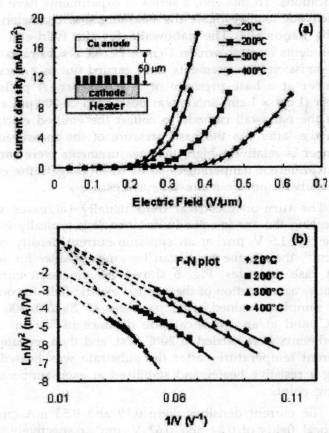

Figure 6. (a) Emission current density as a function of the electrical field at different temperatures for carbon nanowalls, and (b) the corresponding F–N plots of the curves in (a).

The fieldemission characteristics can be analysed using the F-N equation

$$I \propto \frac{V^2}{d^2} \exp\left(\frac{-B\phi^{3/2}}{\beta V/d}\right), \tag{1}$$

where I is the current in Amps, V is the applied voltage in units of Volts, B is a constant given by 6.8×10^7, ϕ is the emitter work function in eV, d is the spacing between the anode and the cathode in units of cm, and β is the geometric enhancement factor. As can be seen in Fig. 6(b), the plots of $\ln(I/V^2)$ versus $1/V$ yielded a straight line which confirmed that the current resulted from field-emission.

This is particularly true for the measurements performed at 300 and 400°C. However, the agreement is not good in the low-temperature curves for which they need to divide the curves into two straight line segments so as to fit the F-N equation. This suggests that there exist two energy barriers with different heights at lower temperatures, which could be caused by the absorbates on the nanowall surfaces. As the absorbate-induced work function change is proportional to the effective field at the absorbate, is not difficult to understand that a higher barrier height was observed at the higher field portion of the F-N plot.

Owing to desorption of the absorbates, the higher barrier portion disappears at higher temperatures. From these plots, they could obtain the slope which is equal to $B\phi^{3/2}d/\beta$, from where the field enhancement factor β could be estimated. Using the work function ϕ of 5 eV, the field enhancement factor β was 31 400, 46 200, 54 800 and 62 900 for the experiments performed at 20, 200, 300 and 400°C, respectively. The temperature dependence is difficult to be understood because the enhancement factor is supposed to be only dependent upon the geometrical shape of the emitter and distance between the cathode and anode.

One may argue that this could be due to the decrease of the work function with the increase of temperature. Note that in this case, the researchers used the lower field portions of the curves for temperatures at 20 and 200°C. As the intersection point dependent upon the work function only, it suggests that the increase of β is not due to the decrease of ϕ. In addition to the temperature-dependence, the value of β at low temperature also one order of magnitude higher than those reported for carbon nanotubes at similar value of cathode-anode spacing.

Further experiments are needed to find out the underlying mechanism for the large enhancement factor. In addition to the temperature-dependent field-emission measurements, experiments were also carried out to study the effects of N_2, H_2, O_2 and CH_4 gases on the field-emission properties of carbon nanowalls at room temperature. The results will be published elsewhere.

The ideal graphite is a semimetal because of its zero bandgap and vanished density of states at the Fermi level. However, the situation changes for nanometer-sized graphene sheets due to the edge and surface effect. This may bring about the nanocarbons' unique magnetic and transport properties. The successful growth of the carbon nanowalls without any catalysts now allows to carry out transport and magnetic property studies of 2D carbons.

Fig. 7 shows the temperature dependence of the resistance in the temperature range from 2 to 10 K at applied magnetic fields of 0 and 400 Oe. As can be seen from the figure, the resistance decreases with decreasing the temperature from 300 to about 106 K, and then shows an upturn at lower temperatures. The temperature (T) dependence of the resistance (R) can be fitted very well using the following equation:

$$R = 0.0018T + 2.5\exp\left(\frac{-127}{T}\right) + 10.8\exp\left(\frac{15.1}{T+34.5}\right) \quad (2)$$

in which the first term represents the metallic contribution, the second term is due to the quasi-1D characteristic of the network structure, and the last term accounts for the hopping/ tunnelling resistance of the junctions. The units of R and T are in Ω and K, respectively.

The junction resistance dominates the total resistance in the entire temperature range, in particular, at low temperatures. Hopping is thermally activated at high temperature, but at low temperature tunnelling is dominant. Also shown in the inset of Fig. 7 is the rate of change of resistance with temperature (dR/dT). The resistance continues to increase with decreasing temperature, reaching the first local maximum at about 4.2 K; after a local minimum is reached at about 3.6 K, it increases again until the temperature decreases to 3 K below which the resistance decreases monotonically until reaching 2 K, which is the lowest temperature of the SQUID setup used in their experiment.

When a magnetic field is applied in the direction perpendicular to the substrate surface, i.e. almost along the surface of the carbon nano-sheets, both local maxima of the curve shift to lower temperatures.

The resistance, in general, also increases with the magnetic field. It is interesting to note that the resistance is not affected by the applied field at temperatures higher than 7 K. The result may indicate that superconducting instability is developed below 7 K in the 2D carbon nano-sheets. For the sake of clarity, the curves are displaced along the vertical axis.

The resistance oscillates strongly with the external field which is applied perpendicular to the substrate surface. The oscillation sets in at about 7 K and its amplitude increases by more than three orders of magnitude when the temperature is decreased from 6 to 2 K. The oscillations are, in general, quasi-periodic; however, the periodicity improves with temperature.

Carbon nanowalls as a Template

The novel surface morphology of the carbon nanowalls makes it an ideal template for synthesising mesoporous materials with high surface areas. One of the possible applications of the carbon nanowalls is in batteries. To this end, they tried to fabricate composites comprised of carbon and magnetic nanoparticles.

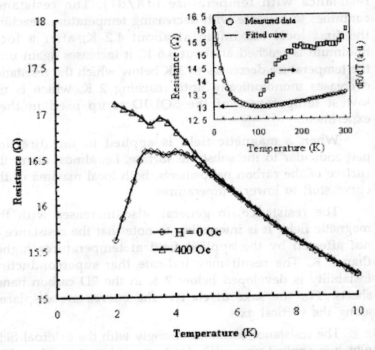

Figure 7. Temperature dependence of the resistance of the carbon nanowalls at low temperature at zero-field and a field of 400 Oe.

This has been done from two different approaches. In the first approach, the nanowalls were used as the adhesive bases to absorb nanoparticles available commercially, whereas in the second approach the nanowalls were used as templates to deposit the nanoparticles using electrochemistry.

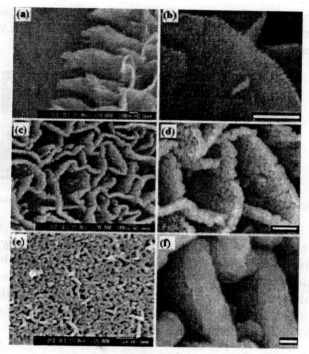

Figure 8. SEM images of Au formed on the carbon nanowall templates at different nominal thicknesses: (a) and (b) 20 nm; (c) and (d) 30 nm; (e) and (f) 100 nm.

Fig. 8 shows the typical SEM images of Au films formed on the nanowall surfaces: (a) and (b), for a nominal thickness of 20 nm; (c) and (d), for a nominal thickness of 30 nm; and (e) and (f) for a nominal thickness of 100 nm. The Au film is in a particulate form when the nominal thickness is 20 and 30 nm, while it becomes a continuous layer when the nominal thickness reaches 100 nm.

It is interesting to see from panel (a) that the nanoparticles formed on the carbon nanowalls are smaller than those formed on the bare substrate just next to the nanowalls. Fig. 9 shows the SEM images of Cu formed on the nanowalls with a nominal thickness of 30 nm.

Comparing with Au, the Cu particles are even smaller on the side walls. The other feature is that continuous Cu wires are formed on the top edges of the nanowalls.

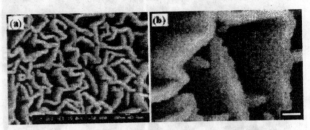

Figure 9. SEM images of Cu deposited on the carbon nanowall templates at a nominal thickness of 30 nm.

The above results demonstrate that, compared with the nanotubes, the nanowalls are more suitable for functionalising purposes which makes them promising for chemical and biological applications. The nanowalls were also found to be good templates for fabricating nanocrystals of certain metals such as zinc.

2D Nanomaterials

In addition to carbon, the researchers also tried to form 2D oxides of transition metals. The general technique that they used was to deposit metal films of appropriate thickness by electrodeposition and subsequently to anneal the sample in air for several hours. The end product ranges from 0D nanoparticles to 1D nanowires and 2D nano-sheets, depending on the starting materials and the anneal temperature.

The 2D nanosheets were found to form from electrodeposited iron and cobalt in the temperature range of 350-500°C. X-Ray diffraction measurements have confirmed that the 2D nano-sheets are Fe_2O_3. In addition to the growth of nanoparticles and films on the carbon nanowalls, it would also be good if one can grow other types of 2D nanostructures on top of the edges of the carbon nanowalls.

Considering the sharp edges of the carbon nanowalls, a natural way to do this is to use electroplating because of the high current density at the edges of the nanowalls. However, the deposition of magnetic materials does not necessarily only originate from the edges but also from other high current density points on the nanowalls, and in most cases nanoparticles or continuous films are formed. Is it possible to form 2D materials following the morphology of the carbon nanowalls?

The solution used is $3CdSO_4:8H_2O$ (61.6 g), H_2SO_4 (19.6 g), SeO_2 (0.062 g), and water (800 ml). The Raman spectrum is dominated by a sharp peak at 256.92 cm^{-1} which suggests that the as-deposited material is amorphous selenium. These types of 2D heterostructures could be useful in increasing the electron-hole separation efficiency when being applied to solar cells.

Single-wall Carbon Nanotubes

Since, the last 50 years, solid-state devices in which electrons are confined to two-dimensional planes have provided some of the most exciting scientific and technological break. From metal-oxide-silicon field effect transistors to highmobility gallium-arsenide heterostructures, these devices have played a key role in the microelectronics revolution and are critical components in a wide array of products from computers to compact-disk players. However, 1-D systems are also proving to be very exciting. For many years, studies of quasi 1-D systems, such as conducting polymers, have provided a fascinating insight into the nature of electronic instabilities in one dimension. In addition, 1-D devices such as "electron wave-guides"—in which electrons propagate through a narrow channel of material-have been created. Experiments on these devices have shown, for example, that the conductance of "ballistic" 1-D systems – in which electrons travel the length of the channel without being scattered—is quantised in units of e^2/h, where e is the charge on the electron and h is the Planck constant. These systems, however, have been limited by the fact that they are inherently complex and/or difficult to make. What has been lacking is the perfect model system for exploring one-dimensional transport—a 1-D conductor that is cheap and easy to make, can be individually manipulated and measured, and has little structural disorder.

Functions of Single-wall Carbon Nanotubes

Some nanotubes are semiconductors. They can therefore be used to construct devices that are one-dimensional analogues of metal-oxide-silicon field effect transistors, in which the electrons move along the surface of a thin two-dimensional layer. Other nanotubes, in contrast, are nearly perfect metallic conductors, and are a new "laboratory" for studying the motion of electrons in one dimension. Both semiconducting- and metallic-nanotube devices are likely to have significant technological applications.

The remarkable electrical properties of single-wall carbon nanotubes stem from the unusual electronic structure of "graphene"—the 2-D material from which they are made. Graphene is simply a single atomic layer of graphite, the material that makes up pencil lead. Graphene has a two-dimensional "honeycomb" structure, made up of sp^2-bonded carbon atoms. Its conducting properties are determined by the nature of the electronic states near the Fermi energy, E_F, which is the energy of the highest occupied electronic state at zero temperature. The energy of the electronic states as a function of their wavevector, k, near E_F is shown in figure 10(b).

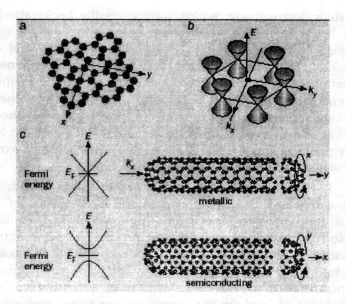

Figure 10. (a) The lattice structure of graphene – the two-dimensional material that is rolled up to form a nanotube. (b) The energy of the conducting states in graphene as a function of the wavevector, k, of the electrons. (c) If the graphene is rolled up around the y axis, the nanotube is a metal, but if it is rolled up around the x axis, the nanotube is a semiconductor

This "band structure", which is determined by the way in which electrons scatter from the atoms in the crystal lattice, is quite unusual. It is not like that of a metal, which has many states that freely propagate through the crystal at E_F. Nor is the band structure like that of a semiconductor, which has an energy gap with no electronic states near E_F due to the backscattering of electrons from the lattice. The band structure of graphene is instead somewhere in between these extremes. In most directions, electrons moving at the Fermi energy are backscattered by atoms in the lattice, which gives the material an energy band gap like that of a semiconductor. However, in other directions, the electrons that scatter from different atoms in the lattice interfere destructively, which suppresses the backscattering and leads to metallic behaviour. This suppression only happens in the y direction and in other directions that are 60°, 120°, 180° and 240° from y (figure 10b). Graphene is therefore called a "semimetal", since it is metallic in these special directions and semiconducting in the others. Looking more closely at figure 10(b), the band structure of the low-energy states appear to be a series of cones. At low energies, graphene resembles a two-dimensional world populated by massless fermions.

To make a 1-D conductor from this 2-D world, we follow the lead of string theorists and curl up one of the extra dimensions to form a tube (figure 10c). The resulting periodic boundary conditions on the wave-function quantises k_n, the component of k perpendicular to the axis of the tube: in the simplest case, $k_n = 2\pi n / C$, where C is the circumference of the tube and n is an integer. The component of k along the length of the tube, meanwhile, remains a continuous variable. If the tube axis is chosen to point in the y direction, the energy as a function of k (i.e. the band structure) is a slice through the centre of the cone.

The tube then acts as a 1-D metal with a Fermi velocity that is similar to most metals. However, if the tube axis points in different directions, such as along the x axis, then the band structure has a different conic section. This typically results in a semiconducting 1-D band structure, with an energy gap between the filled hole states and the empty electron states. The bottom line is that a nanotube can be either a metal or a semiconductor, depending on how the tube is rolled up. This remarkable theoretical prediction has been verified using a number of measurement techniques. Perhaps the most direct was carried out by Cees Dekker's group at the Delft University of Technology in the Netherlands and by Charles Lieber's group at Harvard University in the US.

The Delft and Harvard researchers used scanning tunnelling microscopy to determine the atomic structure of a particular tube — out of the many types of tube that are produced when a sample is grown — before probing its electronic properties with the microscope.

Before we can measure the conducting properties of a nanotube, we have to wire up the tube by attaching metallic electrodes to it. The electrodes, which can be connected to either a single tube or a "bundle" of up to several hundred tubes, are usually made using electron-beam lithography. The tubes can be attached to the electrodes in a number of different ways. One way is to make the electrodes and then drop the tubes onto them. Another is to deposit the tubes on a substrate, locate them with a scanning electron microscope or atomic force microscope, and then attach leads to the tubes using lithography.

More advanced techniques are also being developed to make device fabrication more reproducible and controlled. These include the possibility of growing the tubes between electrodes, or by attaching the tubes to the surface in a controllable fashion using either electrostatic or chemical forces. The "source" and "drain" electrodes—so named in analogy to standard semiconducting devices—allow the conducting properties of the nanotube to be measured.

In addition, a third terminal—called a "gate"—is often used. The gate and the tube act like the two plates of a capacitor, which means that the gate can be used to electrostatically induce carriers onto the tube. A negative bias on the gate induces positive charges onto the tube, and a positive bias induces negative charges. When the conductance of the tube is measured as a function of the gate voltage, two types of behaviour are observed, corresponding to metal and semiconducting tubes. Individual metallic single-walled nanotubes were first studied in 1997 by Dekker's group at Delft and by the author's group at the University of California at Berkeley, both in conjunction with Smalley's group at Rice. Semiconducting behaviour was then reported by the Delft group in 1998. Since then, many groups have made and measured the properties of similar devices. Indeed, most major universities and industrial laboratories, such as IBM, now have at least one group studying these materials for a variety of electronic applications

Nanotube Transistors

Semiconducting nanotubes can work as transistors. The tube can be turned "on" - i.e. made to conduct—by applying a negative bias to the gate, and turned "off " with a positive bias. A negative bias induces holes on the tube and makes it conduct. Positive biases, on the other hand, deplete the holes and decrease the conductance. Indeed, the resistance of the off state can be more than a million times greater than the on state. This behaviour is analogous to that of a p-type metal-oxide-silicon field effect transistor (MOSFET), except that the nanotube replaces silicon as the material that hosts the charge carriers. But why is the tube p-type?

After all, one might expect an isolated semiconducting nanotube to be an "intrinsic" semiconductor—in other words, the only excess electrons would be those created by thermal fluctuations alone. However, it is now believed that the metal electrodes—as well as chemical species adsorbed on the tube—"dope" the tube to be p-type. In other words, they remove electrons from the tube, leaving the remaining mobile holes responsible for conduction. Indeed, recent experiments by Hongjie Dai's group at Stanford University and by the group at Berkeley show that changing a tube's chemical environment can change the level of doping, significantly changing the voltage at which the device turns on. More dramatically, tubes can even be doped n-type by exposing the tube to elements such as potassium that donate electrons to the tube.

The semiconducting device of the type shown in figure 11 is, in many ways, truly remarkable. First, it is only one nanometre wide. While much work has been done to create ultrasmall semiconducting devices from bulk semiconductors, such devices have always been plagued by "surface states"-electronic states that arise when a three-dimensional crystal is interrupted by a surface.

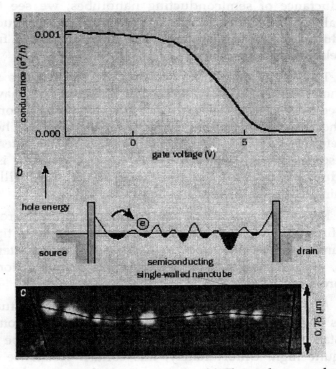

Figure 11. Nanotubes as transistors. (a) The conductance of a semiconducting carbon nanotube as a function of gate voltage. (b) The potential pro.le seen by these holes due to disorder in the structure of the nanotube and imperfect contacts between the electrodes and the tube (c) The tip of a scanning probe microscope can be used to map the barriers to conduction

These surface states generally degrade the operating properties of the device, and controlling them is one of the key technological challenges to device miniaturization. Nanotubes solve the surface-state problem in an elegant fashion.

First, they are inherently two-dimensional materials, so the problem of a 3-D lattice meeting a surface does not exist. Second, they avoid the problem of edges—because a cylinder has no edges! Looking more closely at the conductance of semiconducting nanotubes, we see that initially it rises linearly as the gate voltage is reduced, conducting better as more and more holes are added from the electrode to the nanotube.

The conductance is limited only by any barriers that the holes see as they traverse the tube. These barriers may be caused by structural defects in the tube, by atoms adsorbed on the tube, or by localized charges near the tube. The holes therefore see a series of peaks and valleys in the potential landscape, through which they must hop if the tube is to conduct (figure 11b). The resistance of the tube will be dominated by the highest barriers in the tube.

Recent experiments by the Berkeley and Delft groups con-firm this simple picture. The researchers used the tip of a scanning probe microscope to identify the major scattering sites, thus enabling a map of the barriers to conduction to be produced (figure 11c).

At lower gate voltages, the conductance eventually stops increasing and becomes constant, because the contact resistance between the metallic electrodes and the tube can be quite high. Unfortunately, this contact resistance can vary by several orders of magnitude between devices, probably due to mundane issues such as surface cleanliness.

To improve the consistency of nanotube transistors, many groups are therefore trying to improve the quality of these contacts by developing new cleaning and annealing procedures—with some significant success. These tiny MOSFET-like devices will probably just be the first in a host of new semiconducting-device structures based on carbon nanotubes. Other devices, such as nanotube p-njunction diodes and bipolar transistors, have been discussed theoretically and are likely to be realised soon.

Metallic Nanotubes

In dramatic contrast to semiconducting nanotubes, the conductance of some other nanotubes near room temperature is not noticeably affected by the addition of a few carriers. This behaviour is typical of metals, which have a large number of carriers and have conducting properties that are not significantly affected by the addition of a few more carriers.

The conductance of these metallic nanotubes is also much larger than the semiconducting-nanotube devices, as expected. Indeed, a number of groups have made tubes with conductances that are between 25% and 50% of the value of $4e^2/h$ that has been predicted for perfectly conducting ballistic nanotubes.

This result indicates that electrons can travel for distances of several microns down a tube before they are scattered. Several measurements support this conclusion, including those carried out by our group using scanning probe microscopy. These measurements also show that the contact resistance between the tube and the electrodes can be substantial, just as it is with semiconducting tubes. Further evidence for the near-perfect nature of these tubes comes from the way they behave at low temperatures.

The conductance is observed to oscillate as a function of gate voltage (figure 12). These "Coulomb oscillations" occur each time an additional electron is added to the nanotube. In essence, the tube acts like a long box for electrons, often called a "quantum dot". The electronic and magnetic properties of these nanotube quantum dots reveal a great deal about the behaviour of electrons in nanotubes. For example, the fact that the oscillations are quite regular and periodic indicates that the electronic states are extended along the entire length of the tube. If, however, there was significant scattering in the tube, the states would become localised and the Coulomb oscillations would be less regular.

Nanotube quantum dots that are as long as 10 μm have been found to exhibit these well-ordered oscillations, again indicating that the mean free path can be very long. The experiments described above indicate that electrons can travel for long distances in nanotubes without being backscattered. This is in striking contrast to the behaviour observed in traditional metals like copper, in which scattering lengths from lattice vibrations are typically only several nanometres at room temperature.

The main reason for this remarkable difference is that an electron in a 1-D system can only scatter by completely reversing its direction, whereas electrons in a 2-D or 3-D material can scatter by simply changing direction through a tiny angle. Phonons -long-wavelength lattice vibrations that scatter electrons in both 2-D and 3-D materials at room temperature - do not have enough momentum to reverse the direction of a speeding electron in a 1-D nanotube. They therefore do not influence its conductance, at least not at low voltages.

Recent experiments shown that at high voltages, electrons can emit high-momentum phonons that can scatter electrons in 1-D nanotubes. This leads to a dramatic reduction in the conductance at high voltages, causing the current to saturate at about 25 microamps for a single nanotube. Still, this is a remarkably macroscopic current to be carried by such a nanoscopic system! The fact that a metallic nanotube acts like a near-perfect 1-D conductor at low voltages makes it an ideal system to test some ideas about electrons in one dimension that have been around for half a century. Starting in the 1950s, a series of papers by Sin-Itiro Tomonaga, Joaquin Luttinger and later Duncan

Haldane made it clear that a 1-D electron system should behave very differently from its 2-D and 3-D counterparts when the repulsive Coulomb interactions between neighbouring electrons are taken into account. Under ordinary conditions, a 2-D or 3-D metallic conductor behaves as a "Fermi liquid", even when the electrons interact with each other via the Coulomb force. The electrons in such materials fill the low-energy states up to the Fermi energy, creating what is known as a "Fermi sea" of electrons. The low-energy excitations (or "quasiparticles") of this system act almost like completely free electrons, moving entirely independently of one another.

In other words, an excited state looks very much like a single extra electron above the Fermi sea. In 1-D systems, on the other hand, the low-energy excitations are collective excitations of the entire electron system. The electrons move in concert, rather than as independent particles of a Fermi liquid. This system is referred to as a "Tomonaga-Luttinger liquid" (or, more simply, a Luttinger liquid) to emphasise its difference from the standard Fermiliquid behaviour of 2-D and 3-D metals. One way to test this prediction is to see if an electron can tunnel into the system from the outside world—for example from a metallic contact. If the low-energy excitations are simple quasiparticles, then an electron will have no difficulty tunnelling into the system.

The tunnelling conductance would not be expected to change with temperature or bias voltage. If, on the other hand, the low-energy excitations are collective in nature, the other electrons in the tube must move in concert with the tunnelling electron to make room for it. The electron must literally make a "splash" when it jumps into the Luttinger liquid. If the energy, E, of the tunnelling electron is much higher than the Fermi energy, E_F, then this "splash" is not a problem. As the electron tunnels in with less and less excess energy, however, it has less and less energy to push the other electrons out of the way. Calculations show that the

Luttinger liquid has a tunnelling conductance that decreases in proportion to $(E-E_F)^\alpha$, where α is a particular power. The value of á depends on the strength of the Coulomb interaction between the electrons. It also depends on whether the electron tunnels into the middle of a tube, the end of a tube, or between the ends of two tubes.

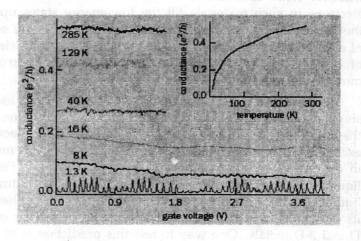

Figure 12. Nanotubes as metals

Theorists have been able to estimate these powers fairly accurately for nanotubes, resulting in very specific predictions that experimentalists can test. The average conductance decreases slowly as a function of temperature (figure 12). The relationship is described by a power law that agrees well with theory. The group has also measured the powers for electrons tunnelling into the middle and ends of a tube, while our colleagues at Delft have done the same for electrons tunnelling from the end of one nanotube into the end of another.

All of these results agree well with the theoretical predictions. These experiments clearly demonstrate that interacting 1-D metals behave very differently to 2-D and 3-D metals.

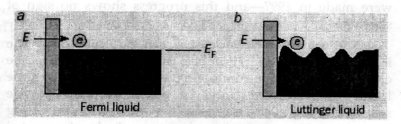

Figure 13. Electrons in one dimension. (a) An electron tunnelling from a metal electrode into a Fermi liquid leaves other electrons in the Fermi sea relatively undisturbed. (b) An electron finds it less easy, however, to tunnel into a Luttinger liquid, because collective excitations in the electron liquid must be excited

This is perhaps not so surprising to use a traffic analogy, car-car interactions are much more important on a one-lane highway than they are in a 2-D parking lot, where a car can move more-or-less independently of the other cars. What is surprising, however, is how long it took before these predictions were tested in detail. While previous measurements of other systems had shown evidence for Luttinger behaviour, nanotubes represent perhaps the clearest and most straightforward realisation of Luttinger-liquid physics to date.

New geometries

While the above experiments demonstrate that many of the basic properties of single-wall carbon nanotubes are now understood, there is an almost limitless number of new geometries and topics waiting to be explored and all manner of new structures to be created. Indeed, researchers are developing a host of new techniques that creatively combine lithography, chemistry and nanoscale manipulation, for example by growing tubes on prefabricated structures or by pushing them around with the tips of atomic force microscopes. It is quite remarkable how far the field has come since the first measurements were made in 1997—and this progress shows no sign of slowing.

For example, new devices can be created by the intersection of two nanotubes, such as a metallic tube crossing over a semiconducting tube. The metallic tube locally depletes the holes in the underlying p-type semiconducting tube. This means that an electron traversing the semiconducting tube must overcome the barrier created by this metal tube. Biasing one end of the semiconducting tube relative to the metal tube leads to rectifying behaviour. In other words, the barrier is overcome in one bias direction, but not in the other. This structure is just one of many possibilities for nanotube devices waiting to be explored.

Meanwhile, Phaedon Avouris and co-workers at IBM's T J Watson Research Center in New York have made "nanotube coils", in which an individual tube loops back on itself to form a ring-like structure. Such coils might be used as tiny solenoids to create magnetic fields or to study quantum interference phenomena. Superconducting contacts have also been attached to nanotubes by several groups to study the behaviour of superconductors connected by a 1-D conductor. Nanotubes also offer great promise as the active elements in "nano-electromechanical" systems.

Their remarkable mechanical and electronic properties make them excellent candidates for applications such as high-frequency oscillators and filters. Many groups have now created devices in which the substrate beneath the nanotube is removed, leaving the nanotube suspended in free space between the two contacts. The tube is therefore free to vibrate like a guitar string, and researchers are starting to investigate the interactions between the mechanical and electronic degrees of freedom.

Chemical Reactivity of Carbon Nanotubes

Single-wall carbon nanotubes have unique mechanical and

electronic properties, which make them promising building blocks for molecular electronics. A major critical issue toward their widespread application in nanotechnology is the control of their electronic properties, which can be metallic or semiconducting in their pristine form, depending on their diameter and chirality.

Since all preparative methods yield mixtures of metallic and semiconducting nanotubes, of different diameters and chiralities, extensive research has been devoted to the modification of electronic structure and the separation between the different electronic types by both physical and chemical processes. The latter requires finding a suitable chemical process that is selective for metallic versus semiconducting carbon nanotubes.

Understanding the interplay between electronic structure and chemical reactivity is thus critical. A few recent research describe some degree of metallic/ semiconducting selectivity toward the noncovalent adsorption of surfactants and single-stranded DNA. The effect of electronic structure on a covalent functionalisation of single-walled carbon nanotubes was recently reported by Strano et al.

The nanotubes reacted with diazonium reagents, which led to addition of aryl groups to the nanotube side-wall. The reaction was highly selective for metallic nanotubes, leaving the semiconducting ones nearly intact, and the reactivity of the metallic nanotubes was inversely related to their diameter. The chemical reactivity of carbon nanotubes had attributed a major role to curvature-induced local strain, which arises from pyramidalisation of the sp^2-hybridised carbon atoms and misalignment of π-orbitals.

The diameter selectivity found by Strano et al. can be correctly predicted by this formalism. However, the metallic/ semiconducting selectivity underscores the role of the electronic band structure in determining the chemical reactivity of the single-wall carbon nanotubes. To account for this selectivity, a reaction mechanism was proposed whereby the diazonium reagent forms a charge-transfer complex at the nanotube surface. Electron donation stabilises the transition state that leads to the decomposition of the diazonium functionality and the covalent attachment of the aryl group to the nanotube.

The extent of electron donation correlates with the density of states at the Fermi level, which is larger for metallic nanotubes. The strength of the pyramidalisation picture is that it presents a chemical view of the electronic structure of carbon nanotubes, which fits into the molecular orbitals description of organic reaction mechanisms. However, it only regards the localised electronic structure of carbon nanotubes, without including in the same molecular orbitals picture the rich and unique delocalised electronic band structure of carbon nanotubes.

Orbital Symmetry and Woodward-Hoffmann Rules

Why and when carbon nanotubes are metallic or semiconducting, which was shown previously in reciprocal space, can also be represented in real space by applying common constructions and concepts used in organic chemistry. A chemical reaction involving the closure of a conjugated system is called an electrocyclic reaction. Thus, the virtual process of rolling up a graphene sheet to form a nanotube could be regarded, from a chemical point of view, as a virtual electrocyclic reaction? Woodward-Hoffman rules are commonly used to describe the stereochemistry of real electrocyclic reactions based on the principle of orbital symmetry conservation. Analogously, we can apply this rule to the graphene roll-up process. To do this with molecules one usually looks at the symmetry of the relevant orbital, that is, the HOMO if it is a thermal process or the LUMO if it is a photochemical process. In fact, there are an infinite number of such valid combinations, but the ones shown here are convenient because they have real solutions and not complex ones.

The LCAO coefficients are obtained by summing up simple sine or cosine functions of the position with the directions and periodicities that correspond to the different G, M, or K wave vectors in the first Brilloiun zone. Note how the degree of bonding varies from the most bonding at the bottom to the most anti-bonding at the top. The two degenerate orbitals in the middle are nonbonding and correspond to the Fermi level. These are the orbitals whose symmetry will determine the properties of the nanotube.

If the graphene sheet is rolled up to form a nanotube in a way that overlaps carbons with similar LCAO coefficients, then the periodicity of the orbital will be conserved in the nanotube, there will be allowed states at the Fermi level, and the nanotube will be metallic. On the other hand, if the graphene sheet is rolled up to form a nanotube in a way that overlaps carbon atoms with different LCAO coefficients, then the orbital symmetry conservation rule will not allow this orbital to exist in the nanotube, there will be a gap at the Fermi level, and the nanotube will be semiconducting.

Since the LCAO coefficients repeat themselves every three translations by any of the lattice basis vectors, a nanotube is metallic when the difference between the indices n and m is a multiple of three, and otherwise it is semiconducting. The advantage of this new real space representation of the electronic structure of carbon nanotubes, besides its illustrative or didactic value, is that it fits in the same framework of organic chemistry that is used to describe the reactions that the nanotubes undergo.

Beyond the virtual process of roll-up, orbital symmetry may play as important a role in real chemical processes involving carbon nanotubes as it does in real pericyclic reactions. The solid-state physics rule of crystal momentum conservation is very important in determining the transport properties and spectroscopy of carbon nanotubes.

The orbital symmetry conservation rule is the molecular equivalent to the crystal momentum conservation rule in the solid state. If this rule governs physical processes, it is likely to govern chemical processes too. In this context, it has been noted that the interaction of carbon nanotubes with metals, which is an important factor determining the nanotube-electrode contact resistance, is related to the matching between the Fermi wavevectors of the nanotubes and the metal. Likewise, for a molecule to interact with a nanotube, there must be a good matching between the shapes of the frontier orbitals of the molecule and of the nanotubes.

Future Development

Single-nanotube devices have come a long way, but how far they will go is anyone's guess. Clearly, they will be part of the scientific landscape for years to come as a model system for studying physics at the nanometre scale. Many commercial applications have also been proposed, from molecular electronics to sensing. Whether these will pan out is more difficult to assess. If these real-world applications of nanotubes are to succeed, we must find ways of successfully integrating them into existing microelectronic products and techniques. But if we manage to develop the technology to fabricate nanotubes of a particular type, length and diameter in a controlled fashion—and to incorporate the tubes into lithographic circuits at particular places with efficiencies approaching 100%—then the sky is, indeed, the limit. While this is a challenging goal, there appear to be no fundamental barriers to achieving it.

10

Microfabrication

Many biomedical applications require delicate surface chemistry that is difficult to achieve with the high temperatures required to bond silicon and glass. Soft materials overcome many of the limitations of silicon discussed above and offer further advantages. Fluidic devices by their nature require more surface area than electronic circuits: The components are larger, and the interface with the external world is more complicated.

The popular silicone elastomer polydimethylsiloxane (PDMS) is 50 times cheaper than silicon on a per volume basis. Elastomers also have a distinctive mechanical property: The Young's modulus can be tuned over two orders of magnitude by controlling the amount of cross linking between polymer chains. Elastomers form a tight seal with silicon and glass, permitting one to design hybrid devices that will contain silicon electronics, light sources, and detectors with silicone fluidics.

Finally, elastomers are a forgiving material to work with, requiring less stringent fabrication conditions than silicon and little capital equipment to set up a fabrication facility. Thus, soft material fabrication has two economies of scale-mass-produced devices will be inexpensive, but it is also affordable to produce small quantities of devices. Rapid turnaround time for fabrication also allows one to quickly iterate and modify designs. Because the cost of entry is low, many people can work in this area, which greatly speeds innovation. An analogous situation is the rapid growth in software due to the development of the personal computer. The other area of consideration is the inexorable march toward smaller feature size and higher integration density.

Although the marked reduction in Young's modulus that accompanies the use of soft materials allows smaller feature sizes for mechanical devices, an even more important consideration is the availability of nonlithographic fabrication techniques for soft materials. The most important of these methods is replica molding, part of a large pool of chemically inspired fabrication techniques developed by Whitesides and co-workers under the rubric of "soft lithography". They have shown a spectacular array of fabrication technologies to make optical components such as blazed gratings, waveguides and lasers, and structures with nontrivial geometry and topology, including three-dimensional conducting coils, linked rings, and basket weave structures.

An embossing technique called "nano-imprint lithography" developed by Chou and co-workers has also shown the ability to fabricate nanometer features and holds great promise for the future. An advantage of replica molding and embossing is that the resolution is determined by the mold feature size, not by the optical diffraction limit. Because the molds are reusable, their cost and fabrication difficulty do not factor substantially into the final cost of a mass-produced device. For example, the molds can be produced with electron beam lithography, a time-consuming and expensive process that has the ability to make nanometer-scale features.

Mechanical Microfluidics

The first functional microfluidic devices made from elastomers performed DNA analysis and cell sorting. These devices used electrokinetic flow control, a popular method used in microfluidic devices made of both hard and soft materials. Although electric fields are a powerful tool for molecular separations, they have drawbacks as a general method of fluidic manipulation.

Electrophoretic demixing occurs when pumping of heterogeneous solutions is attempted. This problem can be partially compensated by alternating plugs of low- and high-conductivity buffer, but other problems then arise. Although the devices work well for fixed conditions, the voltages have to be fine tuned whenever buffer composition or salt concentration is changed.

Voltage control works well for simple devices with only one switching junction, but it quickly becomes problematic to make more complicated devices with many junctions-it is difficult to set the voltages to compensate for the various pressure and resistive imbalances in the devices. These challenges by fabricating mechanical elastomeric valves that have precise fluid control over a wide range of conditions. Choosing an elastomer allowed us to obtain complete valve sealing, low actuation forces, and a small footprint.

These pneumatically actuated valves are surprisingly fast, and we were also able to make peristaltic pumps by arranging three consecutive valves in a row. The valves and pumps have negligible dead volumes and can transport fluid up to a few nanoliters per second, a critical regime for microfluidic assays. They also have very low space requirements; the initial devices were 100 mm by 100 mm, and we have since been able to reduce the active area to 20 mm by 20 mm.

This technology to make a cell sorter with integrated valves and pumps for fluid control (Fig. 1). This cell sorter has more robust performance than the initial device, in that it allows longer running times, higher throughput, and easier integration as a component in complicated fluidic systems. These cell sorters are now being commercially developed and are expected to find applications in a variety of areas, including molecular screening and drug discovery. Besides the cost savings, an important advantage of the microfluidic cell sorters is that they will allow the implementation of sophisticated assays that are impractical to perform with traditional cell sorters or microtiter plates.

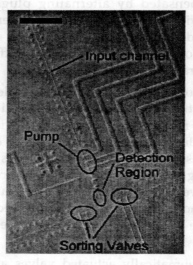

Figure 1. A microfabricated cell sorter with integrated valves and pumps.

The power of soft lithography to show how microfluidics can be used to increase the sensitivity of diagnostic assays. Most diagnostic assays require reagents to bind to solid supports; traditionally, this has been done with enzyme-linked immunosorbent assays (ELISA), and it is expected that these will be complemented in the future by gene expression arrays. In both cases, when probing for multiple targets, the surface area quickly becomes large, and for sufficiently specific reagents, the sensitivity of the assay becomes limited by its ability to pull down all of the analyte in the solution.

Active fluidic pumps can be used to transport analyte material within the binding region of the assay. This allows each of the binding sites to sample all of the analyte, instead of just that portion that can diffuse from a local neighbourhood. To design a chip with a circular channel that could be closed off from the rest of the chip while reagents were pumped within the loop. This design allows complete recycling of the analyte and optimal sensitivity. Such a configuration is topologically impossible to achieve with electrokinetic flow because of the polarities of the electrodes.

A microfluidic print head was used to pattern the surface of a glass cover slip with biotin. The ability of soft lithographic techniques to perform chemical patterning has long been recognised, and early demonstrations showed antibody recognition in microfluidic networks and microcontact printing of self-assembled monolayers. We an designed an elastomeric print head with a radial pattern of fluidic channels and attached it to a glass cover slip whose surface had been functionalised with carboxyl groups.

A biotin-amine conjugate and coupling solution were deposited in a well in the middle, which then filled the microfluidic spokes by capillary action. Although this process only produces a crude pattern with each spoke identically derivatised, more complicated microfluidic networks with active pumping could be designed to distribute reagents in arbitrary patterns. When the biotin coupling reaction was finished, we flushed the channels, removed the print head, and attached the rotary pump. Biotin pixels were thus defined in the regions where the spokes intersected the loop channel of the rotary pump. Micrometer-sized neutravidin-coated latex beads were used as a simulated analyte; the beads have a diffusion constant comparable to a spore, bacteria, or the genome of the bacteriophage lambda. After a solution containing the beads was pumped into the loop, valves at the entrance and exit to the loop were closed.

The beads were then allowed to diffuse within the loop, and after 4 hours, only a small fraction had managed to bind to the pixels. However, when the experiment was repeated with active pumping of the beads around the loop, >80% of the beads in the loop had bound to the biotin pixels within 4 min.

Thus, in this case, active pumping accelerated analyte binding by at least a factor of 60. Devices incorporating such active pumping principles should have markedly increased sensitivity for a wide variety of biochemical assays and should allow efficient affinity purification in chips. Besides the mechanical approach outlined here, more exotic applications of soft materials are being developed. One such area is chemical control of fluidic devices. Beebe and collaborators have shown how functional hydrogel structures can be fabricated in microfluidic channels.

The structures swell or shrink depending on the pH of the solution and can be used to regulate flow control with "chemical feedback." Although these valves are substantially slower than the mechanical valves described above, they are interesting in that they function without external control or circuitry. There is thus the possibility of constructing autonomous, self-regulating devices.

Nanostructured Diffractive Optics

Many biochemical assays create optical signals as output, it is desirable to efficiently couple light into and out of microfluidic chips. One way to accomplish this goal is to include optics near the flow channel. Diffractive optical lenses, beam splitters, and other optical elements can be fabricated both within the glass substrate and within the elastomer material that defines the flow channels. For the latter, it is possible to use the inexpensive replication molding step for high-fidelity pattern definition of optical nanostructures.

It is historically well known that very small surface structures can be replicated with very high fidelity into polymer "replicas". In fact, before the advent of modern scanning electron microscopes, the replication-molding process, followed by shadow evaporation and transmission electron microscopy, formed the basis for microstructural surface analysis. Even higher resolution was available from evaporated carbon replicas.

Nanometer-sized structures can be produced with a replication process, but elastomers, like most organic molecules, are poor conductors. To develop electrical nanodevices, one can use soft materials as templates for fabrication with materials with good electronic properties. Similarly, for nanomechanical applications, we sometimes would like to template a rigid material to achieve high resonance frequencies.

The ultimate limit of template-assisted fabrication is to use a single molecule as a template, and we and others have recently made steps toward constructing molecular nanostructures. Single-molecule nanobridges, electrical point contacts, ultra-small mechanical resonators, and wires have all been demonstrated in efforts to miniaturise functional devices to molecular dimensions. Here, we will compare the lithographic fabrication of nanobridges with a single-molecule templating method.

Electron beam lithography and highly anisotropic pattern transfer have been used to construct nanostructures with lateral dimensions as small as a few nanometers. The ultimate size of the structures is limited in theory by the size of the incident electron beam and forward scattering of the exposing electrons as they interact with the resist and in practice by the resolution of the resist and shot noise in the electron dose. We have fabricated nanopillars only 6 nm in width and lines as small as 10 nm in width by using a combination of high-resolution lithography and anisotropic ion etching.

Although it is possible to construct even narrower pillars, it is very difficult to electrically probe these vertical nanostructures, which are about 60 nm tall and quite fragile. For electrical measurements, it is therefore more desirable to lithographically define the nanowires in plane and use lithographic alignment methods to contact them. When line patterns are lithographically defined in a single-crystal material grown on top of a sacrificial layer, and the sacrificial material is later removed, it is possible to define a conducting bridge.

This surface micromachining method allows the definition of very small suspended structures in almost all of the interesting semiconductor materials systems, such as Si, GaAs, InP, and SiC. The developed fabrication procedures for constructing nanoscale bridges in silicon, where the development of silicon on insulator (SOI) technology for the fabrication of electronic circuits provides us with an ideal starting wafer with SiO_2 as a sacrificial layer.

SOI wafers consist of a thin layer of silicon, which was wafer-bonded onto an already oxidised silicon wafer. Then, we use electron beam lithography and anisotropic etching to transfer narrow lines through the Si layer into the underlying silicon dioxide. To release the bridges from the substrate, samples are then either dipped into hydrofluoric acid or etched in a C_2F_6 plasma. If nanobridges with lateral widths much below 10 nm are to be defined, traditional lithographic techniques are pushed to their limits, and it becomes advantageous to use long molecules such as DNA to construct bridges. DNA has been used as a template to chemically assemble a wire between two electrodes. The DNA molecule was stretched out on a surface and silver was precipitated around it, similar to silver staining of a DNA sequencing gel.

Although the wires were 100 nm wide, much larger than the 2-nm diameter of a single DNA molecule, they already displayed interesting electrical properties. Others have condensed palladium onto DNA to create structures with 40-nm widths and have fabricated comparable structures using microtubules as a template.

One of the attractions of using DNA as a template is the potential for directed self-assembly through the ability of single strands to recognise complementary sequences and hybridise to each other. We have used single molecules of DNA as templates for nanowire fabrication with linewidths below 10 nm.

The fabrication sequence consists of first defining a very narrow trough in insulating material. In this case, an angle-evaporated shadow mask was used to define the trench in quartz. We used molecular combing to stretch single DNA molecules over the trench.

These molecules function as templates and vacuum evaporation was used to deposit a thin layer of gold over the molecules. By exploiting the ability to evaporate at an oblique angle, the channels are not connected electrically. Other structures were found in which the wire was broken, creating a "diving board." The resulting metal wires are some of the smallest resonator structures ever made. Such nanoresonators have an extremely high natural frequency, and calculations show that it may be possible to fabricate mechanical resonators in this fashion with natural frequencies on the order of a gigahertz.

Bottom-Up Manufacturing Techniques

Today the manufacture of very small devices is principally based on top-down manufacturing methods—starting from bigger building blocks, for example a whole silicon wafer, and reducing them to smaller and smaller pieces by cutting, etching, and slicing. Bottom-up manufacturing methods, in which small particles, atoms, molecules, and atom clusters, are added or removed to construct bigger functional structures, are seen by many as the next natural step in manufacture by humans. Bottom- up methods are Nature's way of growing things and in biomimetics one studies how, by building bottom-up, i.e. atom by atom, Nature, through eons of time, developed manufacturing methods, materials, structures, and intelligence.

Bottom-up versus top-down machining

To make small things humans tend to start with large building blocks and use stiff materials (e.g. silicon or stainless steel) whereas Nature prefers small building blocks (e.g. atoms, proteins, RNA, DNA, etc.) and mostly soft, low-Young's-modulus materials (e.g. muscle and skin). As an example of human top-down engineering ingenuity, consider silicon micromachining or MEMS.

Silicon micromachining involves use of Si wafer slabs as thick as 500 μm, insulating layers up to a micron thick, and Al and Au metal layers between a few hundred and few thousand Ångstroms thick. From these, so-called batch fabrication yields hundreds of three-dimensional components from one such wafer. Although MEMS has led to major advances, the method still exploits a limited choice of materials and works with building blocks that are large and crude compared with Nature's arsenal. Further progress in miniaturisation will most probably be based on methods originating in nanochemistry, that is, bottom-up methods and combinations of top-down nanofabrication using "traditional" IC methods and nanochemistry. Over the next ten years the size overlap of objects fabricated with these approaches will become more significant. Consequently, molecular engineers and supramolecular chemists who are manipulating, with rapidly improving dexterity, Nature's building blocks such as atoms, molecules, proteins, and DNA will, jointly with MEMS specialists who are now reaching 0.1 μm lithography limits, find new ways to combine top-down nanofabricated components with bottom-up "natural" products. Because it uses relatively large building blocks, manufacturing by humans is rapid and the expectation is that Nature, because it uses much smaller building blocks, for example, atoms with a diameter of 0.3 nm, must be very slow. To offset the time it takes to work with small, basic building blocks, when an organism grows Nature relies on an additive process featuring massive parallelism and self-assembly. Self-assembly is not yet used much in manufacturing by humans. Some early attempts involved fluid self-assembly (FSA) as practiced, for example, by Alien Technology Corporation.

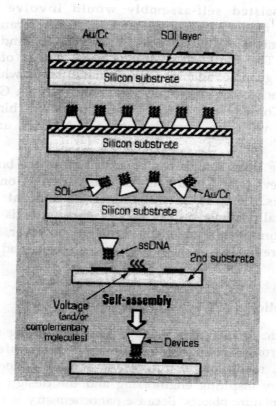

Figure 2. DNA-assisted assembly

In the FSA process, specifically shaped semiconductor devices ranging in size from ten to several hundred microns are suspended in liquid and caused to flow over a surface which has correspondingly shaped "holes" or receptors on it and into which the floating devices can settle. The shapes of the devices and holes are designed so that the devices fall easily into place and are self-aligning. Alien has successfully demonstrated the assembly of tens of thousands of devices in a single process step.

In a yet more daring approach it has been suggested by Esener et al. that one could use DNA tags in so-called DNA-mediated self-assembly. Deoxyribonucleic acid (DNA)-assisted self-assembly would involve taking polymers made with complementary DNA strands and using them as a kind of selective Velcro to bind things together. The short DNA strands used consist of CGAT (cytosine, guanine, adenine, and thymine) bases which will bind to each other in specific pairs only—C with G and A with T. Consequently an ATTTGC strand will bind very strongly with its complement (TAAACG) and not otherwise.

These DNA strands can be coated on to the bottom of specific devices and their complements patterned on to host substrates. This is the chemical equivalent of the geometrical peg-hole system; because these strands actually bond to form their double-helix structure, however, they are much more likely to remain fixed in their exact and desired position.

Biomimetics

Biomimetics is the study of how Nature, building atom by atom, through eons of time, developed manufacturing methods, materials, structures, and intelligence. These studies are inspiring engineering and the design of man-made miniature objects. Because nanochemistry is currently inspiring a new wave of biomimetic efforts, caution is in order, because, as the legend of Icarus so pointedly reminds us, most previous attempts at biomimetics have resulted in failure.

In macroengineering, as S. Vogel points out, human and natural technology form separate, well-integrated entities, operating in an internally coherent context. Nature, for example, does not use steel, nor does it favor the production of flat surfaces and sharp corners -all very useful in manufacturing by humans.

Nature builds with proteins and produces mostly curved surfaces and rounded corners, resulting in such masterfully engineered objects as biological cells. In large-scale engineering projects, natural and human approaches to manufacturing both have their merits within their own proper frame of reference. It is in the nano world that Nature is way ahead of engineering by humans, because it has learned to work with much smaller, more versatile building blocks, and to master the self-assembly of those building blocks.

Nature provides excellent examples in the design of efficient microsystems, because it optimises scaling laws in the micro-domain and even exploits the quantum-size effects of its components. In biological systems, the energy efficiency is approximately proportional to the 2/3 power of the linear dimension. This is because metabolism is proportional to the second power of the linear dimension, and energy uptake is proportional to body volume, so the smaller the organism the greater its efficiency. As a consequence, smallness is the ancestral condition of life. Large organisms are built bottom-up from cells rather than divided into cells. Cells are, in turn, fabricated from yet smaller entities. A single *E. coli* bacterium, for example, is shaped like a cylinder approximately 1 µm across and 3 gm long. It contains at least 3000 different molecular parts and will divide every twenty minutes when nutrients are available.

As one of the many motivating examples of the promise of biomimetics in the nano-domain, consider enzymes. There is a plethora of enzymes that outperform synthetic catalysts by several orders of magnitude. There is, for instance, no man-made catalyst for producing ammonia from its elements at ambient temperature and pressure, as the nitrogenase of nodule-forming bacteria does.

Future Development

Human-made nano devices crafted with bottom-up methods will introduce a much more rewarding paradigm in manufacturing by humans; nanochemistry holds the promise of the versatility of design offered by Nature itself, and molecular self-assembly and replication add to the tremendous appeal of this type of nanotechnology. There is little doubt that biotechnology analysis tools will keep on improving at an increasingly faster rate.

Desktop DNA sequencers and 3D protein readers will be a reality in the not so distant future. Genetic engineering will, however, have the most profound impact on how mankind looks at manufacturing. Because it is already possible to synthesise a virus bottom-up, given the sequence of the bases in its genes, it seems quite likely that we will be able to manufacture synthetic viruses designed to enter a cell and carry out diagnostic and therapeutic tasks. Venter has proposed building bottom-up the minimum gene arrangement required to sustain life in a test tube.

Modern photovoltaic solar cells have a conversion efficiency of approximately 10 to 15% but are expensive to deploy and maintain. Crops grown for energy are also expensive, involve harvesting, and are only 1% efficient. It is conceivable that genetic engineering will enable the production of energy crops that convert sunlight into fuel at 10% efficiency. As a result of nanochemistry the current digital information technology (IT) revolution might well be followed by new analog manufacturing revolution.

Today, computers let us shape our digital environment, but by giving computers the means to manipulate the analog world of atoms as easily as they manipulate bits, the same kind of personalisation might be brought to our physical three-dimensional environment. In this context Gershenfeld from the MIT Media Laboratory envisages a personal fabricator (PF) akin to the PC. A human society based on nanomachining will be much more balanced, with a manufacturing approach based on how the species itself is made.

Products will be based on a fundamental understanding of the assembly of their ultimate components, atoms, molecules, and proteins, and on how to induce self-assembly into useful objects. Materials will be degradable, flexible, and fully re-usable. The smaller building blocks used in manufacture will enable products of more variety and intelligence. There will be less emphasis on traditional engineering materials such as steel, wood, stone, composites, and carbon, and proteins will become much more important. The transition towards a nano-society will require a major shift in workforce skill level, because manipulation of data and application of knowledge of bioengineering will be part of a manufacturing worker's daily duties.

In academia, less hyper-specialisation and better grounding in all the sciences and engineering disciplines will be essential, because the traditional "dry engineering and sciences", for example electrical engineering and mechanical engineering, will merge with the "wet sciences and engineering", for example biology and bioengineering.

Several scientists have speculated that it might be possible to assemble solid particles, e.g. components such as LEDs (light-emitting diodes) on a PC board, by tagging the parts to be assembled with complementary DNA sequences. By mixing these tagged parts and stirring them in a solution, the complementary DNA strands would bind and in the process assemble the parts to which they are linked.

(a) Analyse the mechanism and then describe what you perceive as a major problem with this type of DNA assisted assembly.

(b) How could the situation be improved?

Nanolithography paces the evolution of the integrated circuit industry. Continuing progress by nanolithographers has allowed low-cost, volume manufacturing of sub-micrometer, high-density devices. Success has been stunning, and entire computer systems are now being placed on a single chip, enabling new advanced technologies for computation, communications and entertainment to flourish.

Some more than three decades the timing for introducing new generations of device density has been in agreement with Moore's Law, which states that number of transistors per chip doubles every 18 months. To sustain this pace, the cost of lithography has escalated rapidly and, with the increase a crisis has loomed. Unless the main industrial companies co-operate to map out a workable strategy for developing new lithographic technologies within the total available investment envelope, IC manufacturing will fall behind the road map's schedule and the industrial growth will slow down.

The new nanolithography road map includes a rate reduction announced with the predicted increased size of the microprocessors. The 0.5-μm generation has been dropped from the road map and the 0.1- μm generation has been added. Observers have long forecasted the demise of optical lithography for mainstream IC production technology.

Confounding these predictions, what has in fact happened is the replacement of one optical technology with another of shorter wavelength; g-line (436 nm) steppers have been largely replaced by i-line (365 nm) and deep-UV

(248 nm) steppers are beginning to be inserted into fab areas to address the 0.25-μm generation. Much of the support infrastructure for masks, metrology, and process equipment has been maintained. The difficulties inherent on introducing new lithographic technologies into the fab are illustrated by the relatively slow acceptance of deep-UV lithography.

IC manufacturers are conservative and they resist implementing new technologies until a technology in use can no longer sustain the high device yields. In the case of DUV lithography, this inertia, coupled with an investment higher cost than *i*-line, will delay the introduction of DUV by most manufacturers to the second or third generation of the 64-Mbit DRAM (Dynamic Random Access Memories) or the sixth generation of microprocessors. DUV's slow introduction is an indication for proponents of other technologies. Any new technology should be evaluated in total : technical capabilities and cost of exposure tools, masks, resists and required metrology.

Lithography at 248 nm was long delayed by the unavailability of commercial, robust, high-resolution resist systems. It is still impeded by high resist prices. IC manufacturers, having just introduced 248-nm processes into the 0.25 μm device fabrication, will be reluctant to switch again, for the production of the 0.18 μm generation (1-Gbit DRAM) which is anticipated for year 2001. Unfortunately, simulations show that at the 0.18-μm feature size, the usable depth of focus for high-NA (Numerical Aperture) 248-nm imaging will be less that 0.5 μm. While it is not known whether the process window for 248 nm can be extended for two generations, every attempt to do so will surely be made by IC manufacturers. An attractive alternative to 248-nm lithography uses the ArF excimer lasers at 193 nm. While 193-nm lithography has the potential to give IC makers both a larger depth of focus at 0.18 μm and a higher limiting resolution, extending perhaps as far as 0.13 µm, the current state of the resists sensitive to 193 nm is immature compared to either 248-nm or i-line materials.

A third alternative for 0.18 µm, 1-Gbit generations is the 1 x proximity x-ray lithography. Proximity x-ray sources exist in two principal forms : synchrotron-based and point source. In the former, an electron storage ring supplies x-rays to a dozen or more beamlines; at which a stepper might be equipped with. This could be attractive for large volume DRAM fabrication, but the facility cost would be difficult to justify for low volume applications. More "granular" is the point-source x-ray stepper. "Granularity" refers to point source stepper's small size and cost when compared with a synchrotron source and multiple beam lines. Point source systems to date have been plagued by low exposure power in the wafer plane and linear run-out. System designers hope to solve these problems by developing brighter sources of x-rays and x-ray collimators, using, for example Kumakhov capillary bundles.

Problems and Expectations

A plausible scenario for 0.18 µm production would include the use of 193-nm lithography at the layers requiring the finest resolution and for CD (Critical Dimension) control, typically the gate layer, and 248-nm exposure for other less critical layers. Lithographers are optimistic that high - NA, 193 nm projection systems, supplemented by resolution enhancements such as phase shifting reticles and off-axis illumination, will enable extension of optical lithography to feature sizes of 0.13 µm for the anticipated volume production needs in 2004. The depth of focus and exposure latitude that will ultimately be required for high yield IC manufacturing are still unknown.

Assuming that non-optical lithographic technologies will first find their way into the fab to image critical mask levels at the 0.13 µm level, the industry has less than 10 years to choose between two comparable non-optical alternatives and to develop them for introduction in the process lines. The post-optical lithographic technology for volume device manufacturing will have to satisfy several challenging technical and economical requirements simultaneously:

— tight level-to-level overlay;
— no device damage;
— high resolution over large areas;
— low cost of investment, not exceeding ~35% of total IC manufacturing cost;
— well-developed infrastructure for resists, masks, support equipment, and exposure tools.

At this time, this is the best developed technology which is the most realistic alternative to optics. Research in x-ray lithography spans more than 20 years. Advantages of 1 x x-ray include excellent resist imaging with available DUV resists on all common CMOS substrates, and the ability to extend to 0.1 µm, and possibly below, with the use of very small wafer gaps. The major challenges for 1 x x-ray lithography are tool granularity, mask manufacturability, and commercial availability.

Point source x-ray steppers would be easier to introduce into the fab than synchrotron sources, but may never achieve the flux and collimation needed. Perfect x-ray masks remain nearly impossible to manufacture due to simultaneous requirements for high resolution, tight CD control, precise registration, and freedom from defects.

Extreme Ultraviolet Lithography (EUVL)

Also known as soft x-ray projection lithography, EUVL has generated interest in recent years. Using MoSi multilayer reflectors, one can attain nearly 66% reflectance for soft x-rays at the 13 nm wavelength, enabling the design and construction of projection optical systems based on reflective optics. Advantages of EUVL are its similarity to optical lithography with respect to and exposure tool base. Major challenges relate to optics fabrication and metrology, mask fabrication, and resists. Required tolerances for both the surface finish and the metrology to measure surfaces are an order of magnitude tighter than is achievable today. All materials are strongly absorbing at the 13 nm x-ray wavelength, so surface imaging resist systems are required.

Electron Beam Projection (SCALPEL)

SCALPEL (SCattering with Angular Limitation for Projection Electron beam Lithography) is a promising technology being developed at AT&T. A combination of scanning mask and wafer stages with a scanning electron beam can be used to reduce mask contribution to linewidth control and overlay errors. Commercially available DUV resists are suitable. Due to Coulomb interaction limitations, maintaining high throughput together with high resolution is a key for charged particle projection systems.

Ion projection lithography

This development is being founded by a US consortium, the Advanced Lithography Group.

High-throughput direct-write electron beam lithography

Addressable arrays of negative electron affinity cathodes have been advanced as an approach to improve throughput for electron beam direct-write applications.

Massively parallel arrays of atomic force microscopes (AFMs)

Perhaps the ultimate device in lithography might be achieved by using amorphous Si as a resist in conjunction with a large array of AMFs.

Nanofabrication of DNA Nanostructures

Recently, DNA is to be highly useful as an engineering material for construction of special purpose computers and micron-scale objects with nanometer-scale feature resolution. Properly designed synthetic DNA can be thought of as a programmable glue which, via specific hybridisation of complementary sequences, will reliably self-organise to form desired structures and superstructures. Such engineered structures are inherently information-rich and are suitable for use directly as computers or as templates for imposing specific patterns on various other materials. In theory, DNA can be used to create any desired pattern in two or three dimensions and simultaneously to guide the assembly of a wide variety of other materials into any desired patterned structure.

Given diverse mechanical, chemical, catalytic, and electronic properties of these specifically patterned materials, DNA self-assembly techniques hold great promise for bottom-up nanofabrication in a large number of potential applications in wide ranging fields of technology. Starting with background for understanding why the physical, chemical, and biological properties of DNA make it extremely useful as a "smart" material for nano-engineering projects.

DNA-based nano-engineering as a field is related to computational biology, bioinformatics, and genome informatics rather tangentially; it is more closely allied with biomolecular computation (BMC)—the engineering of biological macromolecules for production of artificial information processing systems. Rather than using binary, electronic computers for analysing information extracted from biological systems, BMC seeks to utilise biomolecules directly as active parts of engineered computers. DNA (deoxyribonucleic acid) is a linear polymer whose monomeric residues are made up of one sugar group (deoxyribose), one phosphate group, and one nitrogenous base (either adenine, cytosine, guanine, or thymine; designated A, C, G, and T, respectively).

The backbone has chemical directionality due to asymmetry in the placement of phosphate groups on the sugar, with each sugar having one phosphate bound to its 5' carbon and one phosphate bound to its 3' carbon. This asymmetry gives the entire polynucleotide chain two distinct ends—the 5' and the 3', as shown in Figure 3.

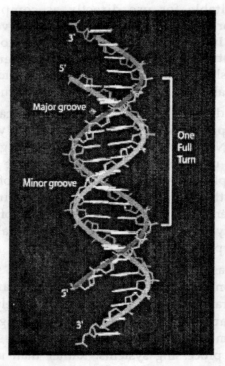

Figure 3. Double-stranded DNA shown in the standard, right-handed, B-form double helix with four base ssDNA sticky-ends appended to the 3' ends of both strands.

Two DNA strands hybridise (form hydrogen bonds) to one another in anti-parallel fashion, thus the 5' end of one strand points toward the 3' end of its complementary strand in the famous Watson-Crick double-stranded form (or double helix). A pertinent point regarding the chemical nature of DNA is that the nitrogenous bases (or simply bases) form hydrogen bonded pairs in tongue-and-groove fashion providing specificity of annealing.

The base groups decorate the sugar-phosphate backbone with regular spacings and provide the physico-chemical energy which zips the DNA together in its predictable helical structure. In double-helical DNA (or double-strand DNA, abbreviated to dsDNA), G bases pair specifically with C residues and A bases pair with T bases. G and C are said to be complementary, as are A and T. DNA strands of exact Watson-Crick complementarity will form stable hydrogen-bonded structures under standard temperature and solution conditions (Figures 3 and 4).

Some alternative base pairings have been found to form fairly stable hydrogen bonding, however, careful design of the sequences, as well as very slow annealing protocols, can successfully avoid alternative pairings and ensure that perfectly complementary strand matchings are highly favoured. If a short segment of single-strand (ssDNA) is appended to a longer strand which participates in a doublehelical domain, the ssDNA will act as a "smart glue", binding specifically to a complementary ssDNA segment located on another ds-domain. These ssDNA segments are known as sticky-ends. Complementary sticky-end pairs therefore act as address labels and can be used to specify which dsDNA domains are allowed to anneal to one another.

Finally, the "folding rules" which dictate the three-dimensional (3D) structure of DNA in solution are simple compared to other biological macromolecules, making DNA a more salutary engineering material than proteins, for example, whose folding rules have yet to be completely understood. Given proper pH and cation concentration,

dsDNA will reliably adopt standard B-form helical structure
with predictable dimensions as shown in Figure 4. The
important points of DNA chemistry include: anti-parallel
alignment of backbones in hybridised strands, base-pairing
specificity for high-fidelity annealing of sequences to their
complements, and annealing by heating and slow cooling
for double helix formation.

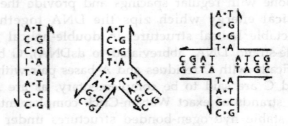

*Figure 4. Representations of unbranched, 3-branched, and 4-branched
DNA.*

The task of engineering specific physical structures from
DNA benefits from the tools evolved during the eons of
biological evolution on Earth and especially from those now
thoroughly researched and commercialised during the more
recent biotechnological revolution. Enzymes can be
purchased which perform highly specific chemical reactions
upon DNA molecules. For example, phosphatases and
kinases remove, add, and exchange phosphate groups from
DNA backbones; ligases stitch together breaks in the
backbone to form a single chemical strand from two or
more shorter strands; and restriction endonucleases cleave
the backbone at specific sites dictated by local base
sequence.

In addition, chemical synthesis methods for the
production of DNA have advanced to the point where DNA
strands of any desired sequence can be ordered on-line
from commercial production companies and shipped the
next day for less than a dollar per residue. Since the

publication of the 3D structure of dsDNA half a century ago, the vast majority of research on DNA structure has centered around DNA as it relates to known biological systems. However, twenty years ago Nadrian Seeman recognised the inherent potential of DNA as an engineering material and proposed visionary new uses for the polymer.

Seeman's pioneering work originally focused on the creation of regular 3D lattices of DNA which could be used as scaffolding for the rapid, orderly binding of proteins to speed the formation of suitable crystals for 3D protein structure elucidation in x-ray diffraction studies. Seeman noted that linear dsDNA can interact with only two other double-helices since it can display at most two sticky-ends, i.e. its maximum valence is two. Construction materials with valence = 2 are only really useful for making linear superstructures like railroad cars connected in a long train.

A larger variety of substructures and an ability to interact with a greater number of neighbouring components is required in order to advance even modest fabrication goals. Seeman pointed out that DNA in biological systems can exhibit structures with increased valence including replication forks (valence = 3) and Holliday junctions found in genetic recombination (valence = 4). One problem with these natural multivalent structures is that they involve repeated base sequences, so base-pairing partners are not perfectly specified and the junctions are mobile. The junctions, or strand crossover points, between the dsDNA domains are free to migrate up or down the helices by swapping one perfect sequence match for another perfect sequence match. Seeman worked out a sequence symmetry minimisation strategy in order to form, for the first time, immobile junctions— branch points in the dsDNA which are unable to migrate up and down the helix.

Note that the oligonucleotides are still normal, linear DNA polymers; the branch junctions occur in the arrangement of strand exchange crossovers between the double helical arms. Seeman has pioneered the use of branched DNA structures for the construction of geometric objects, knots, and Borromean rings. These early construction projects yielded many important technical developments including the use of oligonucleotide assemblies bound to insoluble resin beads for control of construction. One problem with many early DNA constructs was that the structural flexibility of the branched DNA complexes allowed undesired circular products to be formed during assembly of large superstructures from stable substructures. Again, innovation from Seeman's lab solved the problem by producing double-crossover (DX) complexes which act as rigid structural components for assembly of larger superstructures.

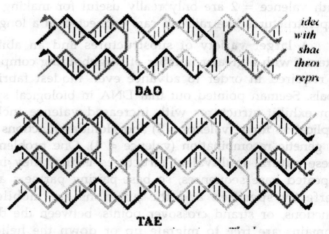

DAO

TAE

Figure 5. Example DX and TX tiles drawn as an idealised projection of 3D helices onto the plane of the page with helix axes lying horizontal on the page

This class of DNA objects, often referred to as 'tiles', contain multiple oligonucleotide strands (ssDNA) which base-pair along parallel, coplanar helix axes. The helices are connected by exchange of two strands at each crossover point.

Rigid and thermally stable, these multi-helix tiles carry multiple, programmable sticky-ends for encoding neighbour relations to dictate tile-to-tile interactions used in specific assembly of patterned superstructures. DNA tiles are formed by heating an equimolar solution of linear oligonucleotides above 90° C to melt out base-paired structures, then slowly cooling the solution to allow specific annealing to form the desired structure.

Tiles are stabilised in solution by the presence of magnesium counter ions (Mg^{++}) which allow close helix packing by shielding the negative charges on the DNA backbones from one another. Design of DNA tiles and superstructures requires two separate phases: first, geometric design and second, chemical or sequence design. The geometric design phase involves modelling and examination of strand topology (paths of the oligonucleotides through the tiles), spacing of crossover points to ensure proper orientation of neighbouring helical domains (for example, to ensure flatness of 2D lattices), lengths of sticky-ends, and overall internal compatibility of components with each other and the superstructure design. Once the geometric constraints of the target structure are established, specific base sequences can be designed which guarantee formation of the desired structure.

Design base sequences for DNA nanoconstruction

To properly design base sequences of DNA for nanoassemblies, one must consider positive as well as negative design constraints: a sequence must not only match its desired hybridisation site, but it must also hold no significant complementarity to any other DNA segment, thus avoiding formation of undesired alternative structures. Many approaches and strategies for sequence design have been pursued.

Primary among design constraints is Hamming distance: no sequence can be included which contains more than some threshold number of exact matches with any other sequence or the complement of any sequence already contained in the set. Thresholds are chosen based on the lengths of sequences required and known limitations from hybridisation experiments. An example constraint might require at least three mismatches between every pair of subsequences of length eight. For longer strands, a sliding window is used to tabulate all subsequences of a given sequence. Such search and design problems require the use of electronic computers to keep track of the huge number of possibilities; therefore, custom software has been developed by several research groups to find good solutions to combinatorial optimisation of sequence design.

Besides Hamming distance, other design criteria include exclusion of certain undesired subsequences for example, palindromes which may form undesired hairpins, long stretches of G and C which, due to stronger base stacking interactions may distort the structure away from standard B-form double helix. Often, homogenisation of base composition within and between strands is desirable in order to increase the likelihood of isothermal annealing. If individual regions of the structure have similar base composition they will have similar melting temperatures and formation of all parts of a tile will occur nearly simultaneously during the cooling process. Careful sequence design is critical for successful assembly of complex objects from synthetic DNA oligonucleotides since base-pair formation is the driving force of the self-organisation process.

Experiments and applications

DNA-based computation: The first experimental proof of the feasibility of DNA-based computing came from Adleman, when he used DNA to encode and solve a simple instance of a hard combinatorial search problem. He demonstrated the use of artificial DNA to generate all possible solutions to a Hamiltonian path problem. For large graphs, the problem can be very difficult for an electronic computer to solve since there are an astronomical number of possible paths and there is no known algorithm for finding the correct answer.

Adleman's approach was to assign a 20-base DNA sequence to each node in an example graph, then to synthesise edge strands containing the complement to the 3' half of a starting node fused with the complement to the 5' half of the ending node for each valid edge in the graph. The sets of oligonucleotides encoding nodes and edges were annealed and ligated, thereby generating long DNA strands representing all possible paths through the graph. Non-Hamiltonian paths were then discarded from the DNA pool, first by size separation of the path DNA, and second by a series of sequence-based separation steps involving DNA probes complementary to each node sequence. By this experimental protocol, Adleman was able to recover DNA strands encoding the Hamiltonian path through the example graph.

The primary contributions of Adleman's seminal paper were the revolutionary concepts that synthetic DNA could be made to carry information in non-biological ways and that the inherent massive parallelism of molecular biology operations could be harnessed to solve computationally hard problems. His experiment showed that DNA could be used as an integral part of a functioning computer. Since that time, some limits have been noted on the size of combinatorial search problems which can be implemented in DNA because of the exponential growth of search spaces and the volume constraints on wet computing techniques. In addition to volume constraints, Adleman's original algorithm involved rather inefficient and tedious laboratory steps, the total number of which increased at least linearly with problem size. These concerns have been sidestepped by more recent theoretical and experimental advances including the development of computation by self-assembly.

Algorithmic self-assembly: Another fundamental insight which has shaped understanding of DNA-based computing and nano-engineering was made by Winfree when he realised that DNA annealing by itself and, specifically, annealings between DNA complexes being developed by Seeman were capable of carrying out computation. This line of reasoning, developed theoretically and experimentally by Winfree in collaboration with Seeman and others, follows a theoretical model of computing known as Wang tiling. In the Wang tiling model, unit square tiles are labelled with symbols on each edge such that tiles are allowed to associate only if their edge symbols match. Tiling models have been designed which successfully simulate single-tape Turing Machines and are therefore capable of universal computation. The recognition that DNA tiles, exemplified by DX and TX complexes, could represent Wang tiles in a physical system, where edge symbols are incarnated as sticky-ends, led to proofs that DNA tilings are capable of universal computation.

Computation by self-assembly of DNA tiles is a significant advance over earlier DNA-based computing schemes because self-assembly involves only a single-step in which the computation occurs during the annealing of carefully designed oligonucleotides. Contrast this with Adleman's experiment in which the annealing step generated all possible solutions and where a long series of laboratory steps was required to winnow the set by discarding incorrect answers. Self-assembly without errors will theoretically only allow formation of valid solutions during the annealing step, thereby eliminating the laborious phase involving a large number of laboratory steps.

A successful computation by DNA self-assembly demonstrated example XOR calculations. XOR, an addition operation without the carry-bit, was performed using tiles carrying binary values (1 or 0) to specifically assemble an input layer which then acted as a foundation upon which output tiles assembled based on the values encoded on the input tiles.

The prototypes also demonstrated the use of read-out from a reporter strand which was formed by ligation of strands carrying single bit-values from each tile in the superstructure. The scheme is currently being extended to harness the massively parallel nature of the annealing reaction by allowing random assembly of the input layers, followed by specific assembly of the output layers in order to simultaneously compute the entire lookup table for pairwise XOR (and eventually addition) up to some modest input length.

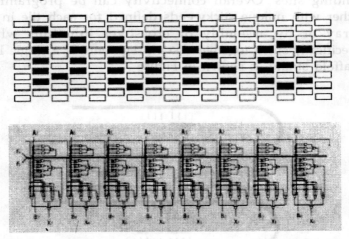

Figure 6. Examples of simple and complex a periodic structures as possible fabrication targets for DNA-based self-assembly.

DNA nanostructure pattern: Programmed self-assembly of DNA objects promises further advances not only in biomolecular computation but also in nanofabrication as a means of creating complex, patterned structures for use as templates or scaffolds for imposing desired structures on other materials. Simple, periodic patterns have been successfully implemented and observed on superstructures formed from a variety of different DNA tiles including DX tiles, TX tiles, triangular tiles, and rhombus-like tiles.

Larger tiles sets with more complicated association rules are currently being developed for the assembly of a periodic patterns which will be used in the fabrication of patterned objects useful for nanotechnology applications (examples are given in Figure 6).

2D tile arrays can be thought of as molecular fabric or tapestry which contain a large number of addressable pixels. Individual tiles can carry one or more pixels depending upon the placement of observable features or binding sites. Overall connectivity can be programmed either with unique sticky-ends defined for each tile in the array or by assembly of crossover junctions which specifically stitch together distant segments of a single long scaffold strand as shown in Figure 7.

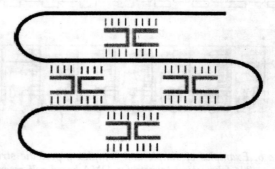

Figure 7. Schematic of a grid structure formed by annealing specific short oligonucleotides (gray) onto a preexisting long ssDNA (black).

Computer simulations and theoretical analysis of self-assembly processes have pointed to some potential difficulties including the possibility of assembly errors leading to trapping of incorrectly formed structures. An experimentally observed error rate of 2-5%, encompassing annealing and ligation errors, was noted in the XOR computational complex. Several approaches exist to address such issues including more complicated annealing schedules, variable length sticky-ends for non-isothermal tile associations, and stepwise assembly controlled by time-stepped addition of critical oligonucleotide components. Read-out methods which sample an ensemble of reporter strands as well as error-tolerant designs for the overall system are also being developed.

Immobilisation on DNA arrays: A variety of strategies and chemistries are being developed including thiols (-SH), activated amino groups, biotin-avidin association, and annealing of pre-bound, complementary DNA. Oligonucleotides, chemically labelled with a thiol group on either the 5' or the 3' end readily bind to gold and have already been used via simple complementary DNA annealing to impart 3D ordering on gold nanospheres and gold nanorods. In those studies, gold was labelled with multiple copies of a single DNA sequence, then linear dsDNA was formed between complementary strands attached to adjacent gold particles. More specific chemistries are available including nanogold reagents which make use of 1.4 nm diameter gold clusters, each functionalised with a single chemical moiety for specific reaction with a thiol or a free amino group.

These reagents have been used to target the binding of single gold nanoparticles to specific locations on DNA nanoassemblies. A similar technique has been reported for construction of a conducting silver wire on a length of ssDNA. Ongoing studies focus on formation of smaller (~10 nm diameter) metal wires laid out in specific patterns on 2D tile lattices.

The long-term goal of these metalisation studies is the self-assembly of electronic components and circuits at length scales below those available by lithography techniques. A novel approach to targeted binding which has yet to be experimentally tested is the display of "aptamer" domains, which have been artificially evolved for specific binding of antibodies (immunoglobulin proteins) to DNA or RNA. Techniques have been developed for in vitro selection of specific nucleic acid/antibody pairs.

The antibody can be utilised as an adapter molecule, binding not only to its DNA epitope displayed on a 2D lattice but also to another protein of interest. The well-known association between biotin and avidin has also been shown to be useful for targeted binding of the streptavidin protein to DNA lattice carrying an oligonucleotide labelled with the small biotin molecule. The development of these and other attachment strategies has just begun. Many advances and new insights can be expected.

Future Applications

Some possible fields of application for future DNA nanotechnologies might include electronic circuit layout, organisation of materials for batteries or flat panel displays, macromolecular patterned catalysts for chemical assembly lines, combinatorial chemistry, sensorless sorting of nanometer-scale objects, DNA sequence comparison, and perhaps gene therapy. DNA self-assemblies may find uses not only in templating nanometer scale electronic circuits alluded to in preceding sections but also in preparation of patterned catalyst arrays. For example, nanoparticulate metals used to catalyse the formation of single-walled carbon nanotubes have previously been used when randomly distributed in aerogels.

Electronic and chemistry: If attachment chemistries can be adapted for the binding of such nanoparticles to DNA tile lattices, then coordinated synthesis of ordered arrays of carbon nanotubes might be possible. Such ordered nanotube arrays might be useful in advanced electrical storage batteries, flat panel displays with ultra-fine pixel density, or very strong, multi-tube fibers. This approach is especially attractive because current synthesis methods generally yield tangled masses of nanotubes which have been difficult to sort and organise. Other target catalysts include protein enzymes or surface catalysts which, when ordered in series, could act as macromolecular chemical assembly-lines. Patterned stripes of catalysts could act sequentially to carry out a sequence of specific reactions or even repeated cycles of reactions on a stream of substrate flowing past.

Combinatorial chemistry: Brenner and Lerner proposed the use of DNA for tagging chemical compounds with specific labels for use in combinatorial chemistry. They suggested that DNA labels could be decoded to reveal the identity of active molecules drawn by a screening assay from a vast pool of candidate chemicals. It is possible that DNA tile structures could be used further to hold chemical reactants close together in space, thereby facilitating their reaction. The product of the reaction would remain bound to the tile, decoding of each strand of the tile would reveal the identity of each reactant used in the formation of active compounds. Encoding labels for reactants rather than final compounds would decrease the number of specific labels required.

Sensorless sorting: Sensorless sorting involves an array of effectors capable of repetitive motion which act to organise objects into specific orientations and move them along a path comparable to a conveyor belt. Carbon nanotubes might be an interesting target object for sorting because they are poorly soluble in aqueous solution and they are difficult to purify and sort yet they are objects of intense study due to their unique structural and electronic properties. A possible scenario might involve a DNA array acting to organise a set of protein rotary motors which then provide a sweeping motion to coax nanotubes into alignment and feed them down a channel. Such an elaborate system could prove useful for simultaneously orienting large numbers of carbon nanotube into position for use as wires in a circuit, for example.

General nanofabrication: Self-assembling DNA-based structures also hold great potential in "seeding" for the autonomous growth of complex structures by bottom-up nano-fabrication. A molecular machine built of and fuelled by DNA has been demonstrated experimentally. The technique introduces the possibility of setting up a cascade of annealing reactions which, once begun, run sequentially without further intervention, and result in formation of a complex structure inaccessible by simple annealing procedures.

Gene sequence comparisons: DNA is also the perfect molecule for comparison of a set of related DNA sequences. If a family of genes (e.g. analogous genes from different organisms) are annealed together with synthetic strands designed to bridge between related sequences, then the existence or the morphology of the resulting superstructure might convey information about the extent of sequence similarity in the gene set.

11

Nanomaterials on Environment

Nanotechnology presents problems in managing risks to human health and the environment. Taking an anticipatory approach to assessing the benefits and regulating the risks from an emerging technology is itself novel. Very little is known about the risks to human health and the environment from nanomaterials, so that a precautionary approach is advocated.

Stopping short of the moratorium on production and use of nanomaterials advocated by some NGO's, restrictions on the technology are recommended including regulating nanomaterials as new chemicals, planning end-of-life management of products containing nanomaterials and a presumption against release of manufactured nanomaterials into the environment. It is now accepted that the conventional separation (in engineering decisions involving risk) between the technical (the province of engineers) and the social (the province of managers, politicians and the public) cannot survive scrutiny.

Failure to recognise the need to manage all aspects of risk including the societal aspects has led to obvious "difficulties" for certain technologies. The nuclear industry is well-known example, as are some forms of biotechnology including attempts to introduce Genetically Modified (GM) crops. Without passing comment on whether these technologies should have achieved public acceptance, it is clear that failure to engage in broad-based debate has introduced problems in achieving satisfactory regulatory bases for the introduction of new technologies, and that once opposition develops it is difficult to overcome. Nanotechnology is an example for which such an approach is needed, given the emergence of public concerns ahead of (and arguably unrelated to) introduction of the technology.

In June 2003, the UK Government commissioned the two principal academies of science and engineering, the Royal Society and the Royal Academy of Engineering, to carry out an independent study into current and future developments in nanoscience and nanotechnologies and their impacts. However, the study was carried out independently of Government, by a Working Group whose 14 members included engineers and scientists, a philosopher, a social scientist, a consumer champion and an environmentalist. The terms of reference included to identify what environmental, health and safety, ethical or societal implications or uncertainties may arise from the use of the technology, both current and future and to identify areas where regulation needs to be considered.

The Report of the Working Group was published in July 2004. Although embodying current thinking in risk management, this approach to examining and planning to manage the risks associated with an emerging technology is itself new. The Royal Society report defies nanoscience as the study of phenomena and manipulation of materials at atomic, molecular and macromolecular scales, where properties differ significantly from those at a larger scale.

Nanotechnologies are the design, characterisation, production and application of structures, devices and systems by controlling shape and size at nanometre scale. In essence, nanotechnology is an emerging technology based on solid particles in the size range where their properties are determined by size and surface condition as well as bulk properties. The principal dimension of a nanoparticle -

e.g. the diameter in the case of a fibre—is typically a few tens of nanometers; i.e. an order of magnitude larger than a DNA strand but of the same order as a virus.

Nanomaterials are already in use in some consumer products, specifically cosmetics and sun-screens. Several of the more immediate possible applications lie in the process and energy sectors. The potential developments in manufacturing arise from the convergence of "top-down" processes such as ultraprecision machining and lithography with"bottom-up" processes based on chemicals and biochemicals; i.e. through a materials revolution combining synthesis and smart fabrication. In the longer term, many of the more interesting possible applications lie in bio-nanotechnology and nanomedicine: implants and prosthetics, improved diagnostics, targeted drug delivery and radiological treatment. Other claims for nanotechnology are more fanciful. A report by the US National Science Foundation and Department of Commerce is cited in the Royal Society/Royal Academy report as a very good example of the difficulty some commentators find in drawing an appropriate line between hope and hype. In support of the US National Nanotechnology Initiative, Roco has claimed it is conceivable that by 2015, our ability to detect and treat tumours in their first year of occurrence might totally eliminate suffering and death from cancer.

The Royal Society/Royal Academy Working Group considered that such a claim demonstrates an over-simplistic view of the detection and treatment of cancer. Concern over damage rather than benefit has been raised by the idea of molecular assemblers, nanoscale machines or "nanobots" able to select and position atoms to assemble an object and thus to replicate themselves.

Hazards and Risks

The current approach to risk assessment contains the scientific elements summarised in Table 2; note that this assessment should form only part of the process of risk management which must incorporate public values. The hazard posed by a substance depends on its inherent properties, while risk assessment also accounts for the probability of exposure of humans and non-human beings to a hazardous substance.

Humans and other beings are routinely exposed to nanoparticles, particularly in the atmosphere originating from natural events (such as volcanic eruptions) and from anthropic activities (particularly combustion processes, including vehicle engines). To some extent, living organisms have developed defences against such particles. However, particles can still penetrate into the body.

For humans, the principle entry routes are via the lungs by respiration, via the skin by dermal exposure and via the gut by ingestion of food and drink. There is some evidence that exposure to nano-sized particles can cause human health impacts, particularly by respiration. The principal evidence derives from epidemiological studies which have indicated an association between particulate air pollution and health, particularly cardiovascular and respiratory disorders.

Largely by analogy with the known effects of asbestos fibres, monofibres are particularly implicated as health hazards. However, their impact will depend at least on their dimensions and on their surface composition and reactivity; i.e. on their properties as nanomaterials. This underlines the conclusion that the health impacts of nanomaterials, along with the other properties that define them as nanomaterials, depend on their size and surface condition.

People using skin preparations such as cosmetics and sun-screens are subject to dermal exposure. Some sun-screens contain titanium dioxide nanoparticles. It is by no means firmly established that they do reduce risks of skin cancer. Furthermore, while there is evidence that nanoparticles cannot penetrate healthy skin, it is not certain that they cannot penetrate lesions.

The likely impact of ingested nanomaterials is unknown, but likely to be less serious than respiratory exposure and probably less of a concern than dermal exposure. Once in the body, it is possible that nanoparticles can cause damage at the neural and cellular level, possibly even penetrating into the brain. The potential impacts of nanomaterials on the environment and non-human species are even more uncertain.

The conventional toxicological approach to assessing ecotoxicity involves exposing organisms—usually daphnia, fish and rats —to the substance in question and observing the dose or concentration at which measurable morbidity results. The results from such tests are then scaled up to give a rough prediction of human toxicity. For nanomaterials, no way of adapting animal exposure tests to show the effect of particle dimensions has been proposed, beyond the obvious approach of testing with particles of different sizes and thereby multiplying the number of tests needed. Only one study appears to have been reported, on the effect of carbon-60 particles on a species of fish, and that study is limited and unsatisfactory.

An alternative approach, still at an explanatory stage, is to observe the effect of a pollutant on cells in culture. Such "in vitro" tests do not appear to have been carried out for nanomaterials, and no protocol has been proposed to examine the effect of particle dimensions. A further approach, sometimes known as "in silico" testing, aims to assess the toxicological potential of chemicals by computer calculation of Quantitative Structure - Activity Relationships (QSARs). QSARs are central to the US approach to risk assessment of chemicals, but the approach does not appear yet to have been developed for nanomaterials although in principle it might be possible to adapt QSAR calculations to allow for particle dimensions. In spite of the general level of ignorance, there are reasons to expect that nanoparticles could interfere with the action of microorganisms, including those in soils.

In the presence of this level of uncertainty, chemical pollutants are conventionally classified according to their persistence in the environment and their propensity to bioaccumulate and hence affect organisms, such as humans, in the higher levels of the food chain.

The tests conventionally applied do not immediately apply to nanomaterials. Given that their properties depend on their surface condition, it is likely that nanomaterials will have limited persistence but this inference remains speculative.

The Rio Declaration on Environment and Development includes the precautionary approach and has subsequently been addressed by various Multilateral Environment Agreements (MEAs) such as the Framework Convention on Climate Change, the Convention on Biological Diversity and its Protocol on Biosafety, the Convention on POPs, etc. As for conventional chemicals, the objectives of risk management and regulation are to eliminate risks to humans and the environment or at least to reduce them to "acceptable levels". Risk results from possible exposure to a hazard. If the hazards associated with exposure and the exposure pathways are unknown for nanoparticles, then risk can only be confined if release is avoided.

For regulatory purposes, this places nanomaterials into essentially the same category as new chemicals. In the EU, new chemicals are at present covered by regulations on the Notification of New Substances (NONS), which require provision of a base data set from which a substance is assigned to a category determining its permitted use before it can be "placed on the market"; i.e. traded or incorporated into products. The data set is placed on a register maintained by the European Chemicals Bureau.

Full risk assessment can be required for chemicals identified as priorities from the base data, but fewer than 30 complete risk assessments have yet been published. Partly in an attempt to improve the rate at which neA chemicals are given full assessment, a new approach to Registration, Evaluation and Authorisation of CHemicals (REACH) has been proposed. However, REACH has been widely criticised, inter alia for being too cumbersome, and it is not clear when it might be implemented.

An approach broadly similar to NONS is followed in Japan, although the classification is made before the substance can be manufactured. The US Toxic Substances Control Act requires the Environmental Protection Agency (EPA) to keep an inventory of all substances regulated under the act, and requires new substances to be notified to the EPA before manufacture or importation. Existing substances produced as nanoparticles are not currently defined as new chemicals.

A precautionary approach implies that the use of nanomaterials requires a high level of risk management unless sufficient information is available to justify a lower level approach. The Working Group recommended that factories and research laboratories treat manufactured nanoparticles and nanotubes as if they were hazardous and seek to reduce or remove them from waste streams and that as an integral part of the innovation and design process of products and materials containing nanoparticles or nanotubes, industry should assess the risk of release of these components throughout the life cycle of the product and make this information available to the relevant regulatory authorities.

Taken together, these recommendations would cover regulation of the supply chain and require protection from exposure to nanomaterials in the workplace. The pressure to avoid risk of releases would have a further implication: it would favour production of nanomaterials at the point where they are incorporated into a finished material or product. This would represent further pressure towards small-scale distributed production of high value chemicals and materials. The explicit mention of the life cycle also leads to the important conclusion that products containing nanomaterials must be managed after use to ensure that none of these materials can escape into the environment.

The specific recommendation is that manufacturers of products that incorporate nanoparticles and nanotubes and which fall under extended producer responsibility regimes such as endof- life regulations be required to publish procedures outlining how these materials will be managed to minimise human and environmental exposure. This recommendation represents an extension of one of the stated objectives of "takeback" legislation such as the EU Waste Electrical and Electronic Equipment (WEEE) and End-of-Life Vehicles (ELV) Directives: to require manufacturers to design systems for recovery and management of products at the end of their service lives. It has been argued that the way these Directives have been implemented has failed to have this effect.

Thus, if the recommendation is implemented seriously, it could actually improve management of material cycles and promote the development of industrial ecology. With products such as cosmetics, sun screens and food additives in mind, the Working Group recommended that ingredients in the form of nanoparticles undergo a full safety assessment... before they are permitted for use in products; that manufacturers publish details of the methodologies... used in assessing the safety of ... products containing nanoparticles; and that the ingredients lists of consumer products should identify the fact that manufactured nanoparticulate material has been added. This obviously supports the EU's general approach to regulation and disclosure rather than that used in the USA. But it would go further and put regulation of cosmetics on a basis approaching that applied to pharmaceuticals.

Pursuing the logic further, the Working Group recommended that until more is known about environmental impacts of nanoparticles and nanotubes... release of manufactured nanoparticles and nanotubes into the environment be avoided as far as possible. If implemented, this recommendation would immediately prevent any activity which deliberately involves unconfined release of nanomaterials, including the use of nanoparticles to improve combustion of hydrocarbons in engines and of iron nanoparticles for soil remediation by injecting them into groundwater. Both technologies using nanoscale materials and the anticipatory approach to assessing the benefits and regulating the risks from an emerging technology are at an early stage: nanotechnology has yet to make a serious economic impact outside the R and D community.

It is therefore important to avoid the uncritical over-enthusiasm which has characterised some of the advocates of nanotechnology. However, the need to manage and regulate risks in the face of uncertainty is a general problem. New technologies involving new materials will continue to present the kind of difficulty raised by nanoscale materials: lack of epidemiological evidence, lack of systematic toxicological evidence and possibly lack of suitable testing protocols.

A precautionary approach is intended to avoid the impacts on human health and the environment which are the topic of epidemiological studies, so that effective regulation should ensure that epidemiological evidence never does become available. Risk management will therefore increasingly depend on limiting exposure rather than substituting materials with lower inherent hazards.

Combustion and thermal processes are dominant sources of air pollution. Although much attention is still paid to their contribution to priority air pollutants; ozone, volatile organic compounds (VOCs), and nitrogen oxides (NOx) also produce chronically toxic products of incomplete combustion (PICs). The green house gas, carbon dioxide, is a product of complete combustion of carbon and the ozone promoter, NOx, is a product of complete combustion of nitrogen. However, chronically toxic organic pollutants, such as benzene, PCDD/F, acrylonitrile, and methyl bromide, are products of incomplete combustion of carbon, carbon and chlorine, carbon and nitrogen, and carbon and bromine compounds, respectively.

Although these toxic combustion by-products are be formed in many types of combustion and thermal processes, they have historically been of particular concern for incineration of hazardous wastes and soils/sediments contaminated with hazardous wastes. For this reason, on-site incineration, defined by direct contact of the waste material with a flame, has come into disfavour. Instead, thermal destruction or desorption (in which the waste does not directly contact the flame) has been frequently substituted. Unfortunately, low or moderate temperature treatment has the potential to form more toxic by-products than incineration. While some of these pollutants are emitted in the gas-phase, they are frequently associated with fine and ultrafine PM.

Since so many pollutants are associated with fine particles and fine particles have been strongly implicated in pulmonary and cardiovascular disease, much research has focused on their health impacts. Multiple theories have been proposed for the observed health impacts of fine and ultrafine PM; however, there is increasing evidence for induction of oxidative stress as the progenitor for many of the observed illnesses. PAHs, CHCs including PCDD/Fs, BHCs including mixed brominated/chlorinated dioxins (PBCDD/Fs), toxic and redox active metals, and persistent redox-active free radicals have been found to be associated with combustion generated PM and been suggested as responsible agents for one or more observed health impacts.

Emisssions of Toxic Combustion Byproducts

The nature of combustion by-products are determined by the chemicals that are treated and the conditions under which they react. Although incinerators, catalytic oxidizers, thermal desorbers, and accidental fire scenarios are quite different from an engineering perspective, the underlying reaction chemistries that form pollutants are closely related.

Chemical reaction zone theory

Toxic combustion by-products include two broad categories of organic pollutants that are defined under the Resource Conservation and Recovery Act of 1976 (RCRA). They are residual, undestroyed emissions of so-called Principal Organic Hazardous Constituents (POHCs) that are contained in the feed-stock and Products of Incomplete Combustion (PICs) that are formed during the thermal treatment. In addition, toxic metals may be vaporized and emitted; however, they more frequently react with oxygen or chlorine resulting in a change in chemical form and oxidation state. Few, if any, organic components of the feed-stock survive direct contact with the flame and other than soot, only minimal organic by-products are formed. Thus the vast majority of the observed pollutants in the effluent must be originating from chemistry occurring outside the flame.

In fact, most of the pollutants are probably formed in the high-temperature, post-flame zone or at even lower downstream temperatures as a result of surface-mediated reactions. In the most general sense, the mechanisms of pollutant formation and destruction are expected to be relatively consistent within a zone. This "Zone Model" allows for classification of the reactions occurring within a given zone (Figure 1).

Zone 1, the pre-flame, fuel zone, is characterised by a wide range of temperatures (near ambient to 1200°C), residence times on the order of 0.1 s, and low excess air conditions. Because this zone occurs at the front end of the device, it creates new reaction intermediates by several low energy, unimolecular reaction pathways such as HCl elimination and carbon-halogen bond rupture that react further in the downstream zones.

Zone 2, the high-temperature, flame zone, is characterised by temperatures of 1000-1800°C at which essentially every organic compound will undergo complete conversion to its most thermodynamically stable end-products, viz. carbon dioxide, water, hydrochloric acid, and nitric oxide. Under local pyrolysis conditions soot is the dominant product.

The flame zone generates large quantities of vaporised metals, and chlorine that are very important reactants in subsequent zones. Observed organic pollutants are likely due to flow-paths that pass through the periphery of the flame or flow eddies of poor fuel/air mixing. These flow-paths represent destruction "failure modes" of the flame and generate pockets that are more properly described as high-temperature thermal zones, viz. Zone 3. Zone 3, the post-flame thermal zone, is a chemistry-rich zone where various types of radicalmolecule reactions occur. It is characterised by temperatures from ~600-1100°C, residence times of a few seconds, and both oxygen rich and oxygen depleted regions.

Experimental and modelling studies indicate that the majority of the pollutant formation in this zone occur in oxygen-depleted pockets of poor waste-air mixing. Within this zone most of the PAHs, higher molecular weight CHCs, BHCs, and mixed bromo/chlorocarbons (XHCs) are formed by molecular growth pathways. This zone may also be where metals vaporised in the flame zone are condensed to ultrafine particles. Zone 4, the gas quench, cool zone, exists downstream of the flame and post-flame zones and is characterised by either gradual or rapid quenching of the gas temperature. Residence times are long, >10 s, and oxygen concentrations vary from oxygen depleted, due to combustion in upstream zones, to oxygen rich zones if air in-leakage occurs.

Partially oxidised products such a formaldehyde, chloroformaldehyde, and phosgene forms by radical-oxygen association reactions. Nitrated products form via radical-molecule addition reactions involving NO_x generated in the flame zone. Hydrocarbons and chlorocarbons may also be partially oxidised in this zone resulting in the emissions including oxy-PAH and oxy-chloro-PAH. Zone 5, the surface catalysis, cool zone is fundamentally different from the other four zones in that one must now consider the effects of surfaces at temperatures between 200 and 600°C.

Reaction times for gas-surface reactions are a few seconds for entrained particulate or hours for deposited particles. PCDD/Fs have been shown to be formed in Zone 5. However, many more pollutants potentially form as a result of surface catalysis via pathways including CHCs, BHCs, and XHCs;PBDD/F and PXDD/F; partially oxidised hydrocarbons and CHCs (i.e., carbonyls, alcohols, organic acids, epoxides); as well as nitro-PAH, oxy-PAH and oxy-chloro-PAH. Most of the reactions necessary to form these products require a transition metal catalyst. That the Zone 2 and 3 reactions that form nanoparticles of soot/flyash also transform metals into catalytically active forms and catalyse the formation of new toxic by-products in Zone 5.

Once formed in Zone 5, the temperatures are too low to result in their destruction and the pollutants are emitted into the atmosphere. Incinerators and accidental fires contain all these zones. Thermal destruction devices contain only Zones 3, 4, and 5. Thermal desorbers consist of low temperature components of Zone 3 as well as Zone 4 and 5. Catalytic oxidisers consist of Zones 4 and 5, only.

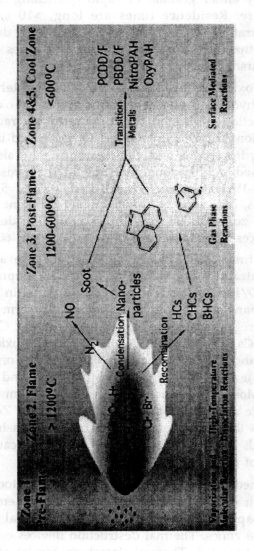

Figure 1. Combustor Reaction Zones. Zone 1-Preflame, fuel zone.

The omission of Zone 2 in most ways increases the probability of pollutant emissions by allowing all of the waste to react in Zones 3 through 5, rather than destroying a large portion of it in the flame zone. Unfortunately, non-incineration, thermal technologies, and fires are not subject to the same strict testing and regulatory scheme as incinerators. Consequently, most emissions of toxic combustion by-products remain uncontrolled for these sources. However the problem is not intractable because:

1. There are only a limited number of products that form from the direct oxidation or pyrolysis of a given compound.

2. In addition to by-products from specific precursors, full-scale emissions characterisations, pilot-scale and laboratory studies have shown that there are certain "ubiquitous" by-products that form regardless of the waste being burned.

3. The conditions under which pollutant forming reactions occur are well defined within the zone theory of pollutant formation.

These principles suggest that characterisation of toxic combustion by-products may be studied in a systematic scientific manner. In addition to PAH that are formed in virtually every combustion source, we now believe that the principal classes of pollutants from the combustion/thermal degradation of hazardous wastes are: i) fine and ultrafine particles, ii) chlorinated hydrocarbons/brominated hydrocarbons, and iii) persistent radicals.

Fine and Ultrafine Particles: Ultrafine, or nanoparticles, are largely formed by combustion sources as primary particulate emissions or as secondary particles formed by atmospheric chemical reactions of combustion emissions of sulfur and nitrogen oxides.

Nanoparticles are not efficiently captured by air pollution control devices (APCD), are transported over long distances, and penetrate deep into the respiratory system, all of which enhance the potential health impacts. Metals are vaporised in the flame-zone and subsequently nucleate to form small metal nanoparticles or condense on the surfaces of other nanoparticles in transit to the post flame (thermal reaction) zone (Figure 1 & 2). Under pyrolytic or oxidative pyrolysis conditions at temperatures above ~ 600°C (Zone 2), the metal seed nuclei promote reactions with gas-phase organic species to form a carbonaceous layer resulting in nanoparticle growth (Zone 2-3). Below ~ 600°C, under primarily oxidative and oxidative pyrolysis (thermal reactions in the presence of trace quantities of oxygen) conditions, the metal nuclei or surface-condensed metals initiate formation of new gas-phase and particle-associated pollutants (Zones 3-5).

Elemental carbon (mostly soot) and organic carbon (the myriad of organic chemicals) account for over half of these particles. Although ~80 % of the organic carbon is extractable, only 12% are chemically resolved. PAH, oxy-PAH, alkanes, organic acids, and macromolecular species similar to humic acid make up the majority of the identified chemicals. These airborne particles also contain percent (e.g., Fe, K, Si) and ppm (e.g., Cu, Ni, Zn) concentrations of transition, alkali, and other toxic metals. Redox-active metals (e.g., iron and copper) and organics (e.g., PAH, oxy-PAH, and semiquinones) have been implicated in the biological activity of airborne fine and ultrafine particles. However, numerous studies have also implicated. Unfortunately, the organic fraction remains largely uncharacterised; and there is little-to-no data on speciation of metals and the presence of metal-organic complexes that undoubtedly exist in these particles.

Emissions of Chlorinated and Brominated Hydrocarbons: The combustion and thermal reactions of CHCs, are of particular interest because they constitute the majority of the toxic components of hazardous wastes; they are often quite refractory; and they form other highly toxic, aliphatic and olefinic CHCs, chlorinated PAH and PCDD/F. Trichloroethylene produces a wide range of by-products, including hexachlorobenzene, chlorinated PAH, and the perchlorinated analogue of the highly carcinogenic butadiene. CHCs also form as by-products in the Zone 5, by surface mediated reactions. This finding, along with the resistance of CHCs to oxidation, suggests that ClPAH/PAH formation may be more facile in halocarbon combustion systems than hydrocarbon systems.

Numerous research studies have definitively demonstrated that PCDD/F are formed in almost any combustion or thermal device if there are sources of carbon and chlorine along with a transition metal to catalyse chlorination and condensation reactions. Three general pathways of formation have been proposed: 1) de novo formation (200-500°C) in which carbon in soot or fly-ash acts as reagent to form PCDD/F by chlorination/oxidation of "dioxin-like" structures that inherently exist in a carbon matrix, 2) transition-metal, surface-catalysed formation (200-500°C) from PCDD/F precursors such as chlorinated phenols and chlorinated benzenes, and 3) gas-phase, radicalmolecule reactions (>600°C) of chlorinated phenols, chlorinated benzenes, and polychlorinated biphenyls (PCBs).

Field studies suggest that gasphase pathways are responsible for about 30 % of total PCDD/F emissions, with the remainder due to surface-mediated pathways. Any source containing a hydrocarbon, a transition metal and a source of chlorine (organic or inorganic) will form PCDD/Fs if the temperature is ever raised above 200°C. There is a growing recognition that brominated hydrocarbons, including PBDD/Fs, are formed and emitted during the thermal treatment of brominated flame retardants in fabrics and plastics and electronic materials (E-materials and E-wastes), frequent contaminants at Superfund sites. Until recently, BHCs have received little attention primarily due to difficulty of analysis, lack of available analytical standards, and a paucity of health effects data.

However, recent findings suggest that brominated flame retardants as well as PBDD/Fs are highly toxic. Computer motherboards contain an incredible amount (~50% per unit)of bromine).Analysis of the effluent from an E-waste incinerator reveals that the effluent contains 4.6-7.6 mg/dscm of copper. This is significant because it is well established that copper catalyses the formation of PCDD/F from CHCs in combustion system and the same catalytic behaviour is expected from BHCs. Recent experimental studies have shown that BHCs, PBDD/Fs, mixed BCHCs, and mixed PBClDD/Fs are formed from combustion of E-material. It is clear that our understanding of the environmental hazards of emissions of BXCs is only in its infancy, and further progress is hindered by lack of understanding of the basic combustion chemistry and availability of analytical standards for toxicological, chemical, and combustion evaluation.

Emissions of Persistent Free Radicals: Reports of persistent radicals in coals, chars, and soots date back to the 1950's. Although a link between free radicals in these samples and health impacts was suspected, their potential health impacts were not recognised because they were thought to be "inaccessible to cells and too stable to play any part in carcinogenesis" until the publication of a series of papers by Pryor demonstrating the viability of catalytic cycles involving semiquinone radicals.

However, persistent free radicals are present in combustion-generated fine and ultrafine particles and that these radicals induce DNA damage. Using EPR we have found that combustion of 10 different fuels and CHCs produced semiquinone type radicals that are stabilised on the particle surfaces. Semiquinone radicals are known to undergo redox cycling to produce biologically damaging

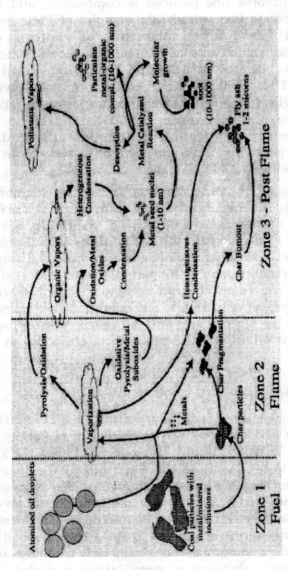

Figure 2. Nanoparticle formation/growth and mediation of pollutant forming reactions in combustion systems.

superoxide and hydroxyl radicals. Because the principal source of airborne fine particles is combustion, and these sources generate free radicals, the samples of $PM_{2.5}$ from 6 cities and found large quantities of radicals with characteristics similar to semiquinones. Aqueous extracts of combustion-generated particles and $PM_{2.5}$ samples induced damage to DNA in human lung epithelial cells and myeloid leukemia cells. $PM_{2.5}$-mediated DNA damage was abolished by superoxide dismutase (SOD), catalase, and desferoxamine, implicating the superoxide radical, hydrogen peroxide, and the hydroxyl radical in the reactions inducing DNA damage.

Identical DNA damage was caused by incinerator bottom ash. The source of this damage is a surface-associated semiquinone-type radical. Semiquinones are relatively non-reactive with O_2 due to resonance stabilisation. When a semiquinone is adsorbed on a surface, additional stability may be imparted to the radical if the adsorption site is an electron acceptor. The presence of semiquinone-type radicals on combustion-generated particulate is significant and suggests a previously unrecognised origin of the health effects attributed to fine particulate.

Health effects

Routes of Exposure and Distribution - Size Matters: Combustion of hazardous wastes results in pollution that exists in a gaseous, liquid, and/or solid particle state suspended in air. A crude characterisation of suspended pollutants utilises the mean diameter of the suspended particles and varies from a few nanometers to several microns. The coarse fraction, ≥ 50 microns, of suspended airborne pollutants originates from windblown dust, crushing and grinding operations, materials handling, and/or atmospheric abrasion of even larger particles. The aerodynamic diameter of inhalable coarse particles ranges from 2.5 - 10 μm (i.e., PM_{10}). Combustion, on the other hand, typically generates smaller particles that are <2.5 μm in diameter (i.e., $PM_{2.5}$). Finally, ultrafine particles, or nanoparticles, are formed in both combustion sources and in the atmosphere processes through condensation and molecular growth pathways and are <100 nm (i.e., $PM_{0.1}$) in diameter.

Particles are deposited in the respiratory tract; and deposition is directly proportional to aerodynamic diameter of the particles (Figure 2). PM_{10} deposits mainly in the upper respiratory tract and may be cleared by mucociliary actions. $PM_{2.5}$ and $PM_{0.1}$ penetrate the alveolar regions of the lung where the ultrafine particles rapidly penetrate the epithelium. Clearance of fine and ultrafine particles is mediated mainly by phagocytic activity and particle dissolution.

The ability of $PM_{0.1}$ to translocate to the pulmonary interstitium suggests that these particles have a significant impact on the health of other organ systems. Indeed, studies using radio-labelled 2, 3, 7, 8 tetrachlorodibenzo-p-dioxin ([^{3}H]TCDD) have clearly demonstrated that inhalation, ingestion, or dermal absorption resulted in major tissue deposits of [^{3}H]TCDD to the liver and fat and suggest that multiple routes of exposure occur and that these exposures lead to multiple organ and systemic effects.

Ambient air pollution is a complex mixture of volatiles and particulates arising from various sources including vehicular exhaust, flaring of hydrocarbons at refineries, coal burning at power plants, and thermal treatment of hazardous wastes at Superfund sites. A larger number of epidemiological studies have documented associations between air pollution, specifically $PM_{2.5}$ and $PM_{0.1}$, and acute health effects. However, very little is known about the health effects associated with exposure to the by-products produced from the combustion of hazardous wastes. Thus, the following discussion is primarily based on a review of recent literature addressing the effects of air pollution on health effects.

Pulmonary effects

Decreased Lung Function: Increases in ambient air pollution result in increased hospital admissions for numerous respiratory endpoints including decreased lung function (i.e., reductions in peak flow and declines in forced expiratory volume in 1 second (FEV_1)), cough, and exacerbations of pulmonary disease states such as asthma and chronic obstructive pulmonary disease. Interestingly, stratifying the results of some of these studies for gender demonstrated an increase in asthma attacks in girls as compared to boys. However, none of these papers even postulate as to why females may be more susceptible to air pollution than males.

Inflammatory Responses: Exposure to airborne PM has been shown to elicit an acute inflammatory response (i.e., an influx of neutrophils and other inflammatory cells in the airway lumen and release of proinflammatory cytokines) in the lung. Effects of air pollution on pulmonary function are observed in various animal models including rats, mice, and dogs. In a recent study, normal rats exposed to concentrated ambient air particles ($PM_{2.5}$) for three consecutive days demonstrated a dose-dependent increase in pulmonary inflammation, as measured by increased neutrophil numbers in the bronchoalveolar lavage (BAL) fluid. These data were supported by histopathology demonstrating an acute inflammatory response characterised by an influx of neutrophils into the central areas of the pulmonary acinus, hyperplasia of the alveolar epithelium, and macrophage accumulation in the alveolar spaces.

Immune Responses: Data further suggest that ambient air pollution has the ability to modulate immune responses due to certain respiratory viral infections. PM_{10} exposure has been shown to interfere with the replication of

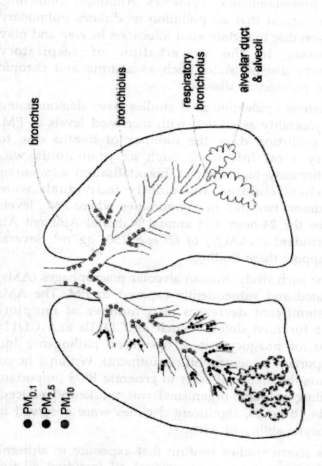

- PM$_{0.1}$
- PM$_{2.5}$
- PM$_{10}$

bronchus

bronchiolus

respiratory
bronchiolus

alveolar duct
& alveoli

Figure 3. Distribution of PM in the airways. Fractions ≥ 100 îm in diameter enter the nose and mouth.

respiratory syncytial virus and lead to a decreased production of proinflammatory cytokines. Whereas, exposure of rhinovirus-infected epithelial cells to moderate levels of air pollutants led to enhanced generation and release of proinflammatory cytokines. Although conflicting, these data suggest that air pollution modulates pulmonary inflammation due to certain viral infections in vivo and may be important in the exacerbation of respiratory inflammatory disease states such as asthma and chronic obstructive pulmonary disease.

Numerous epidemiological studies have demonstrated increased mortality associated with increased levels of PM. On high pollution days the number of deaths due to respiratory viral infections such as pneumonia was disproportionately high. In fact, hospitalisation admissions for pre-school children and elderly individuals were elevated almost two-fold in communities where PM_{10} levels were above the 24-hour and annual National Ambient Air Quality Standard (NAAQS) of 65 and 150 $\mu g/m^3$. Several studies support these findings.

In one such study, human alveolar macrophages (AMs) were isolated and subsequently exposed to PM. The AMs showed significant decreases in a number of receptors important for host defense such as CD11b and CD11c (important for phagocytosis of opsonised pathogens) and CD29 (important in neutrophil recruitment). Within 3 hours of exposure, the ability of AMs to generate ROS (important in the killing of micro-organisms) was markedly reduced, and within 18 hours, significant declines were observed in the phagocytic ability of AMs.

More recent studies confirm that exposure to airborne particles from combustion of residual oil (residual oil fly-ash, ROFA) may alter AM function. For example, ROFA instilled into the trachea of rats prior to infecting them with Listeria monocytogenes results in an increase in the phagocytic ability of AMs, decreased bacterial killing, and increased mortality. These results correlated with a significant decrease in the production of nitric oxide (NO) by AMs. The demonstrated suppression of host defense mechanisms against L. monocytogenes is not specific to ROFA or PM, but has also been observed upon exposure to sulphur-related air pollution leading to longterm respiratory effects and to changes in AM-mediated particle clearance mechanisms.

While the above studies are in agreement with numerous other studies on ROFA and bacterial infectivity, they are in disagreement with assessments of infectivity using other particulate samples. For example, AM function (i.e., phagocytosis and production of ROS) was actually enhanced in the lungs of animals exposed to crystalline silica and subsequently infected with L. monocytogenes. The reasons for this controversy are unclear; however, it is anticipated that the various components associated with the source of the PM are important in the observed effects. Cumulatively, these data suggest that air pollution acts as an immunosuppressor deflating the normal host response to pathogens and in particular the pulmonary immune response. Whether this is a result of decreased AM cell numbers, decreased AM phagocytic abilities, and/or diminished T cell responses appears to be dependent on the chemical composition of the exposure.

Diminished Lung Function Growth: Although effects on pulmonary function are obvious, longterm effects such as lung function growth in children are just being realised. Gauderman and colleagues followed a cohort of 1,678 fourth grade schoolchildren from 12 different southern California communities over a period of 4 years. Each spring a team of Children's Health Study technicians obtained 7 maximal forced expiratory maneuvers on each child as a measurement of pulmonary function. Air pollution in the 12 communities was monitored for the entire study period. Air monitoring stations recorded hourly concentrations of ozone, PM_{10}, and nitrogen dioxide levels. $PM_{2.5}$ levels were obtained from 2-week filter samples. Investigators observed a negative correlation between pollution levels and pulmonary function for all pollutants examined. A significant negative correlation was observed between FEV_1 growth rate and acid vapor (p=0.03). Significant negative correlations between $FEV_{25-75\%}$ were observed for acid vapor, nitrogen dioxide, $PM_{2.5}$, and elemental carbon. Despite the large number of publications in this area, no resounding theory as to how ambient particulate matter induces pulmonary dysfunction has surfaced.

Cardiovascular effects

Increased Cardiovascular Events: Epidemiological studies have also shown an increase in cardiovascular morbidity and mortality that is associated with increases in PM. In fact, cardiovascular deaths were higher than pulmonary deaths during peak episodes of air pollution. Numerous studies conducted within the United States and other countries including Canada and Chile have reported statistically significant, positive correlations between daily human cardiovascular events and exposure to fine particulate matter in the atmosphere.

Unfortunately, the epidemiological data do not provide a clear description of the types of cardiac events observed. In fact, cardiovascular deaths in the majority of these studies were lumped into a single group, coronary heart disease (CHD), which was associated with increases in ambient particulate concentration. However, CHD results from myocardial ischemia, arrhythmias, arthrosclerosis, thrombosis, and/or vascular spasm. This represents a major problem in determining the underlying cause of cardiovascular mortality associated with increased PM levels.

The temporal association between cardiovascular hospitalisations/mortality and ambient PM seems to be relatively short (0-3 days) suggesting that increased cardiovascular morbidity/mortality is due to myocardial ischemia, myocardial infarcts, and/or ventricular arrhythmias and heart rate variability. Short-term exposures (<2 hours) have been shown to increase the occurrence of myocardial infarction in people at risk of developing CHD. Numerous animal studies have been able to replicate the majority of the observed human responses to PM. These studies demonstrate that acute exposure to environmentally relevant PM induces cardiovascular effects including changes in heart rates; arrhythmias; electrocardiographic abnormalities; cardiomyopathic changes, including inflammatory infiltrates, fibrosis, and cardiac myocyte degeneration; and progression of atherosclerotic lesions.

Chronic Cardiovascular Inflammation: Long-term exposure studies (10 mg/m^3 at 6 hour/day and 1 day/week for 16 weeks) demonstrated that PM induces both time- and dose-dependant myocardial injury in Wistar Kyoto (WKY) rats. Histopathology of the cardiac tissue revealed randomly distributed foci of inflammatory responses composed of mixed populations of neutrophils, lymphocytes, and macrophages and suggests a state of chronic-active inflammation in the heart due to PM exposure. The myocardial injury was characterised by cardiac myocytes in various stages of degeneration.

The degenerating cardiac tissue was associated with fibrosis and collagen accumulation of the interventricular septum and throughout the ventricles. Interestingly, examination of the pulmonary tissue showed a dose- and timedependent accumulation of particle-laden AMs with no associated peribronchial or perivascular inflammation or pulmonary fibrosis, suggesting that PM directly affects cardiovascular tissue.

A recent study using dogs residing in polluted urban areas of southwestern Mexico City demonstrated numerous myocardial changes including apoptotic myocytes and inflammatory infiltrates in the left and right ventricles and interventricular septum. Vascular changes were also noted in the dogs including smooth muscle cell hyperplasia, deposition of PM in the media and adventia, and microthrombi in the capillaries and small arteries and veins.

Very little is known about how PM increases the risk of cardiovascular events. One hypothesis is that inhaled PM produces an acute cardiovascular event indirectly through the induction and perpetuation of inflammatory responses in the lung.

The chemokines and cytokines released during this inflammatory response travel through the blood to the myocardium where they are known to cause myocardial dysfunction including myocardial infarction, atherosclerosis, and decreased contractility. Indeed a systemic inflammatory response induced by PM has been demonstrated. This systemic response elicited cytokine release from the lung into circulation and proliferative responses of bone marrow polymorophonuclear leukocytes. In conjunction with the systemic inflammation, it was noted that a progression of atherosclerotic plaques occurred upon exposure to PM in animals susceptible to atherosclerosis.

An alternative hypothesis is that the inhaled PM is absorbed by the blood and translocated from the lung to the heart. Provocative data from a few investigators have begun to demonstrate the ability of $PM_{0.1}$ to penetrate deeply into the lower respiratory tract where it is capable of producing significant systemic effects and to diffuse from the lungs into the systemic circulation. Evidence for transport of PM from the lungs into circulation was noted, although not discussed, in the canine study, which demonstrated deposition of PM in the arteriolar blood vessels. PM transported via the vasculature, directly or indirectly, influences the cardiac myocytes, cardiovascular functioning, and/or hemodynamics through thrombus formation or changes in rhythm.

Reproductive effects

Exposure to environmental pollutants has also been linked to adverse reproductive health. Some of the effects observed include developmental changes in the male reproductive tract including testicular abnormalities, while other effects include reduced fecundity (i.e., reduced sperm quality and count, reduced levels of testosterone, and embryo implantation). Studies using organochlorines, which are found in the diet of Inuit tribes from the Arctic, have demonstrated decreased motility and diminished viability of sperm within 2 hours of exposure. If exposure occurred during in vitro fertilisation, the investigators observed diminished sperm penetration of the oocyte and slower development to blastocyst rates. Likewise, decreases in female fertility have been observed upon exposure to environmental air pollution.

Female mice exposed to ambient air for a period of four months displayed higher incidences of implantation failure and decreases in live-born pups. These differences in fertility were significant if exposures to ambient air pollution began at an early age (i.e., 10 days after birth). Cumulatively, these studies suggest that pollutants affect implantation and reduce fertility by damaging the germ-line cells.

Toxicity of Nanoparticles and Fibres

To understand the potential risks to humans from nanoparticles, it is necessary first to consider briefly the body's defences against particles in general and the properties that particles require to overcome these defences. Throughout much of their evolutionary history, humans have been exposed to small particles, often in very high concentration, and the mechanisms evolved for defence against micro-organisms are also used to defend the body against such particles. Access to the human body can occur through the lungs, the skin or the intestinal tract. Each organ presents a barrier to penetration by micro-organisms or other particles. Nevertheless, despite the defence mechanisms outlined certain particles have proved to have toxic effects on humans, just as have certain microorganisms. These mechanism as follows:

Lungs

In the lung, small particles may be filtered out of the inhaled air by deposition on the airway wall and removal to the throat by the rhythmical beating action of microscopic protrusions (cilia) from the lining cells of the airways, or they may reach the gas-exchanging tissues and be engulfed by phagocytic cells called macrophages. These cells then carry the particles up the airways or through the lungs to lymphatic vessels and thence to lymph nodes. Both mechanisms tend to remove the particles from areas where they have the potential to cause harm and to neutralise their toxicity. However, an overwhelming dose may lead to excessive inflammation, scarring and destruction of lung tissue, as exemplified by bacterial pneumonia or industrial lung diseases such as asbestosis.

Gut

The epithelium of the gut differs from the other external epithelia in that its primary function is to allow absorption of substances into the body. However, unless diseased, it is impermeable to large molecules such as proteins (the largest of which are tens of nanometres in size), which it needs to break down before absorption, and to particles and micro-organisms.

The high acidity of the stomach has an important microbicidal function, as well as a digestive one, and may dissolve some particles and affect toxins in various ways. The lower gut has a highly specialised secretory and absorptive epithelium that produces mucus and digestive enzymes and is richly supplied with blood and lymphatic vessels, allowing it to recruit defensive cells and remove penetrating microorganisms if necessary.

Research into better formulations for drug delivery has shown that some nanoparticles may be taken up by gut lymphatic vessels. Much disease of the gut relates to infections and to adverse reactions to foods. Environmental and occupational causes of diseases of the gut, other than these, are uncommon. In general this is a consequence of properties that either allow them to evade or cause damage to defensive mechanisms.

An understanding of these mechanisms is of importance to estimate the possible toxic effects of nanoparticles or nanotubes. Three types of particle in particular have provided relevant information: the minerals quartz and asbestos, and the particles associated with air pollution.

a)   *Quartz*: Quartz is a mineral to which many millions of workers have been exposed, for example in mining and stone working. Exposure for a few years to micrometresized particles, in concentrations of the order of a milligram per cubic metre of air, leads to a potentially fatal form of lung fibrosis. Toxicological studies have shown that relatively low exposure to micrometresized particles of quartz causes severe lung inflammation, cell death, fibrosis and tumours in rats. This has been demonstrated to be related to the surface of the quartz crystal, which is highly reactive and generates free radicals (reactive atoms or molecules), leading to oxidative damage to the defensive cells that take up the particles. It is likely that this surface activity is a fundamental aspect of the toxicity of particles but one that varies considerably between different types of particle.

Other mineral particles encountered in industry, such as coal and various silicates, are less toxic but are still capable of causing similar diseases when inhaled in higher doses. It is now believed that inhaled particles in general, even when they have a low intrinsic toxicity to cells, may cause disease of the lungs if the dose is sufficiently high by overloading the lung defences, and that this property relates to the total surface area of the particles inhaled. Thus mineral particles have demonstrated that the toxic hazard is related to the surface area of inhaled particles and their surface activity. The risk relates to the dose inhaled.

b)   *Effect of asbestos:* Inhalation by workers of this natural fibrous mineral is known to cause several different diseases of the lung and its lining (the pleura), most of which prove fatal. Fibres are defined as particles with a length at least three times their diameter. Fibres narrower than about 3µm have aerodynamic properties that allow them to reach the gas-exchanging part of the lung when inhaled, whereas those longer than about 15µm are too long to be readily removed by macrophages. Once lodged in the deep lung, their toxicity depends upon an ability to initiate an inflammatory reaction, involving attraction of macrophages and other defensive cells, which, if sufficiently widespread, may eventually lead to scarring (asbestosis) and lung cancer.

Over decades, migration of fibres through the lung to the pleura in sufficient numbers leads to the development of mesothelioma, a fatal tumour. Studies in rats have shown that the likelihood of a fibre, be it asbestos or some other natural or man-made fibre, to cause these diseases depends critically on its solubility.

Fibres that dissolve readily are likely to break into shorter particles that are easily removed by macrophages, and so are unlikely to persist long enough to cause such diseases. This has been supported by studies of human lungs, which have shown differential persistence of different fibre types in exposed workers with asbestos-related diseases. Asbestos is present in the fabric of many buildings and in cities, and all of us have some in our lungs.

In contrast, those who develop asbestos-related diseases usually prove to have millions of fibres in every gram of lung tissue as a consequence of cumulative exposure to concentrations of several hundred fibres in every breath when they are exposed to the mineral at work over months or, more often, years. Thus, studies of asbestos and other fibres have shown that their toxicity depends on the two physical factors, length and diameter, and two chemical factors, surface activity and durability (ability to resist degradation). Again, the risk relates to the dose reaching the target organ.

c) *Air pollution*: Any combustion process produces nanoparticles in vast numbers from condensation of gases. Initially only about 10nm in diameter, these rapidly coalesce to produce somewhat larger aggregates of up to about 100nm, which may remain suspended in the air for days or weeks. The sources of such combustion nanoparticles range from volcanic activity and forest fires, to the use of fires for heating and cooking, and more recently industrial and traffic pollution. Modern scientific interest in air pollution started after the disastrous London smog episode in December 1952, when some 4000 excess deaths occurred over a two-week period.

Particle concentrations were as high as several milligrams per cubic metre, and most of these particles were in the nanometre size range. Reductions in pollution as a result of legislation to restrict coal burning have prevented such serious episodes from occurring subsequently in UK cities. Nevertheless, from the 1980s, a series of epidemiological studies has provided evidence that exposure to the particulate fraction of air pollution is associated with both heart and lung disease and is still responsible for measurable morbidity and mortality in urban areas as outlined as follows:

— Death from and exacerbation of heart disease in vulnerable people.

— Death from and exacerbation of chronic lung disease in vulnerable people.

— Exacerbations of asthma.

— Long-term increase in risk of death from heart attack and lung cancer.

— Possibly, precipitation of cot death and stroke in vulnerable individuals.

Air pollution is caused by a complex mix of particles and gases. However, there appear to be consistent associations between exposure to the particulate fraction and adverse health effects. In seeking to explain these, two difficult facts have had to be considered. First, the concentrations associated with measurable effects on health in populations are extraordinarily low—for example, rises of only $10\mu g/m^3$ are consistently associated with an increase in cardiac deaths of about 1%. Secondly, the particles comprise chemicals generally believed to be nontoxic, mostly carbon and simple ammonium salts. It seemed unlikely that inhalation of less than a milligram of nontoxic particles over 24 hours (a human breathes about $20m^3$ per day and urban concentrations average about $20\text{-}30\mu g/m^3$) could cause a heart attack.

Consideration of this problem led to the hypothesis that the adverse heart and lung effects are due to the action of the nanoparticulate component of the pollution on susceptible individuals, reflecting the point made above for quartz: that the total surface area and the surface activity hold the key to toxicity. Although the mass concentration of nanoparticles is low, it still amounts to some tens of thousands of nanoparticles per millilitre of urban particle counts. This concentration implies that one inhalation of 300ml will contain several million such particles, over half of which will be retained within the lungs.

Activities such as cooking, driving in traffic or being in the presence of smokers entail breathing much higher concentrations. Since all are exposed yet few suffer adverse effects, it is generally believed that air pollution exerts its adverse effects on a minority of individuals who, because of prior illness, are particularly susceptible. The concept that nanoparticles in air pollution might be responsible for the observed adverse health effects has promoted interest in their toxicology, and this interest is expanding rapidly.

This toxicity is largely explained by the presence of transition metals on the surfaces of some types of nanoparticle and their subsequent ability to promote release of free radicals in contact with body tissues However, other nanoparticles with no transition metals appear to achieve their effects by their large surface area and the ability of this surface to generate oxidative stress on cultured cells or isolated organs (in vitro) or directly on laboratory animals or humans (in vivo) by as yet unknown mechanisms.

A few specifically designed epidemiological studies on human populations have investigated the cellular reactions demonstrated by in vitro and in vivo toxicology. However, it is often difficult to attribute responsibility to one or other component of the air pollution, and air pollution particles themselves are of differing chemistry and likely to include metallic atoms and molecules that will influence their toxicity.

In general, epidemiological studies of air pollution point towards the finer particles rather than the coarser causing harm, although gases such as nitrogen oxides (which correlate closely with particle number) also show associations with several negative health impacts. Observations linking air pollution episodes with cardiac responses and with changes in heart rhythm and sometimes blood pressure have led to suggestions that, as well as a humoral (or blood-borne) response, a short-term neural response to air pollution may occur.

The mechanism for a response by the nervous system is not clear and is currently an area of active research. Nanoparticles would be a strong candidate (though not the only one: gases might have such an effect) for the role of initiator of the neural reflex; viruses may use nerves for transmission, and recent work has suggested that manufactured nanoparticles may penetrate and pass along nerve axons and into the brain. There is also some evidence that metals characteristic of air pollutants may be found in the brains of urban dogs, and it is possible that transfer of particles along the nerves concerned with smell may provide a transport mechanism. More research on the neurotransmission of nanoparticles is needed. The most significant finding from research into air pollution particles for the hazard of nanoparticles is that cells and organs may demonstrate toxic responses even to apparently nontoxic substances when they are exposed to a sufficient dose in the nanometre size range.

Natural Environment and Non-human Species

It is plausible that soil or water organisms could take up manufactured nanoparticles escaping into the natural environment and that these particles could, depending on their surface activity, interfere with vital functions. The evidence that nanoparticles may inhibit motility and phagocytosis of macrophages, for example, suggests that similar effects might be expected on simple soil organisms. As with human toxicology, the dose to which the organisms are exposed would be expected to be critical in determining toxicity. In common with other chemicals, nanoparticles may reach humans and other organisms by a wide variety of environmental routes.

Organisms may ingest materials that have entered the water system or been deposited on vegetation. The criteria used to identify chemicals that have intrinsic properties that give cause for concern about their potential to damage the environment (or human health through the environment) are based on persistence, bioaccumulation and toxicity. Chemicals that score highly according to all three criteria are of particular concern.

Once inhaled or ingested, materials may enter the food chain, leading to the possibility of bioaccumulation and ingestion by organisms higher up the chain. Exposure by ingestion therefore depends on the persistence of the material (that is, its longevity in the environment) and its potential to accumulate, usually in lipids.

Measures of persistence and bioaccumulation indicate when levels of a chemical are likely to build up in the environment and how difficult it will be to return concentrations to background levels if a problem is identified with the chemical. Bioaccumulation will depend on the surface properties of nanoparticles, which will determine whether they are likely to be taken up by the fatty tissues, bone or proteins in the body.

The C_{60} particles used in the study on largemouth were bass lipophilic, indicating that they could be taken up by fatty tissues. Persistence will depend on whether the material decomposes, for example by oxidation, and on whether the particles are modified in the environment, for example by agglomerating or adhering to other materials so that they lose the particular properties that could make them hazardous as nanomaterials. For animals, simple tests for persistence and bioaccumulation are used for preliminary screening to identify chemicals whose risks may give cause for concern.

In addition, there are numerous tests for toxicity. Whether these simple tests can be adapted for nanoparticles and nanotubes needs to be established and, if not, alternatives need to be developed. More generally, there is a need to establish appropriate methodologies for testing the toxicity of substances in nanoparticulate form in the context of both the environment and human health. Currently, almost nothing is known about the behaviour of nanoparticles in the environment (for example, whether they agglomerate and how this affects their toxicity); the only information on how they are transported through environmental media such as soil and water comes from initial studies on their potential for remediation, which indicate that nanoparticles of iron can travel with the groundwater over a distance of 20metres and remain reactive for 4-8 weeks.

A current source of environmental exposure is in the waste streams from factories and research laboratories. Until more is known about the environmental impacts of nanoparticles and nanotubes, we are keen to manage any potential risk by avoiding their release into the environment as far as possible.

One of the difficulties in determining potential future exposure of the environment and humans to manufactured nanoparticles is the lack of information about both the extent to which they will be used in products and also the likelihood of such particles being released from nanomaterials such as composites in a form or quantity that might cause harm to humans or the environment. Any widespread use of nanoparticles in products such as medicines (if the particles are excreted from the body rather than biodegraded) and cosmetics (that are washed off) will present a diffuse source of nanoparticles to the environment, for example through the sewage system.

Whether this presents a risk to the environment will depend on the toxicity of nanoparticles to organisms, about which almost nothing is known, and the quantities that are discharged. Perhaps the greatest potential source of concentrated environmental exposure in the near term comes from the application of nanoparticles to soil or waters for remediation.

In some cases the nanoparticles used for remediation are confined in a matrix but, in pilot studies, slurries of iron nanoparticles have been pumped into contaminated groundwater in the USA. Given the many sites contaminated with chemicals and heavy metals, the potential for nanotechnologies to contribute to effective remediation is large.

But this potential use also implies a question about eco-toxicity: what impact might the high surface reactivity of nanoparticles that are being exploited for remediation have on plants, animals, microorganisms and ecosystem processes? It is of course possible that, in the concentrations used in remediation, any negative impacts on ecosystems will be outweighed by the benefits of the clean up of contaminated land and waters, but this needs to be evaluated by appropriate research and further pilot studies before deliberate release into the environment is allowed. In the UK, requests for use of nanoparticles in remediation of groundwater and other contaminated media are likely to be made to the Environment Agency. The nanoparticles might be used to increase the bioavailablity of pollutants, allowing them to be broken down by bacteria, or that they might be used to disperse and dilute pollutants. .

Nanomaterials in Plastics

In plastics especially, nanocomposites, i.e., resins with 2% to 5% loadings of nanoclays or carbon nanotubes, are an important new means of upgrading physical properties. Key benefits include barrier improvements in packaging, higher stiffness and dimensional stability in molded parts, flame retardance, and electrical conductivity. Many industries are aggressively pursuing the technology with a new generation of higher-performing products.

But the growth of nanocomposites in plastics and other applications is not without controversy. There are concerns about the toxicity of nanomaterials and the environmental impact they may have throughout their life cycle and that of the products incorporating these materials. Research is under way in government, academia, and industry to assess the safety of nanomaterials, and some environmental groups are calling for a moratorium on further commercialization of the technology.

Nanotechnology applies to particles ranging in size from 1 to 100 nanometers. In plastics, nanoclays come in platelet form and are usually 1 nm thick with aspect ratios of 1 to 1000. Carbon nanotubes are generally 1 nm in diameter. Based on figures from Nanotech Plus, a market research and consulting firm in Stamford, Connecticut, 25 million to 30 million lbs of finished polymers in North America, with a value of $85 million to $100 million, incorporate nanomaterials.The international nanotechnology market is growing, fueled by R&D investments. According to the U.S.

National Institute for Occupational Safety and Health (Niosh), global investment in nanotechnology by governments alone rose to about $3 billion in 2003 from $432 million in 1997. By 2015, Niosh projects, the value of nanotech-related products will exceed $1 trillion worldwide. Environmental concerns about nanotechnology do not, for the most part, include plastics, at least not yet. Because nanomaterials are encapsulated within resins, they do not raise the same safety issues as products that make direct contact with people and the environment.

In health care, for example, nanometals are introduced into the body for disease detection, imaging, and treatment. Work is also under way on using nanoparticles as delivery systems in vaccines and agricultural fertilizers. Concerns extend, as well, to product disposal, where researchers are evaluating the potential of nanomaterials to separate from products and enter the environment as free particles.

Concerns about nanomaterials in plastics are mostly focused on worker exposure during handling and processing, and the impact of free particles on air quality in labs and plants. While there is as yet no conclusive evidence that nanosized materials are more dangerous than larger versions of the same materials, experts believe that we should exercise caution. "There is some compelling evidence that nanomaterials need to be examined as nanoparticles," says Kristen Kulinowski, executive director of the Center for Biological and Environmental Nanotechnology (CBEN) at Rice University in Houston. "It cannot be assumed that they have the same chemical properties as larger particles of the same material."

CBEN, funded by the National Science Foundation, spe- cializes in analyzing the effects of nanoparticles on aqueous systems. Kulinowski says that work by CBEN and other organizations suggests that size matters when it comes to environmental impact and the potential toxicity of nanomaterials. The field of nanotechnology is still so new, at least for artificial materials (nanoparticles also occur in nature), that there has been no time to develop substantive data on exposure and hazards.

"Toxicologists didn't think about nanomaterials five years ago," says Kulinowski. End-users have been applying regulatory criteria for conventional materials to their work with nanosized versions. In plastics, many experts see no indication that clays along with carbon nanomaterials pose a problem. "Are current methods for evaluating industrial toxicity acceptable?" asks Brauer of Nanotech Plus.

One key concern about nanoparticles is their potential to invade the body, either through skin contact or by inhaling airborne particles. Niosh, among others, reports that nanomaterials can penetrate the skin as well as translocate from the respiratory system to other organs. It also states that ultrafine particles "are more toxic than larger particles on a mass-for-mass basis." There is additionally the extent to which free particles affect the environment.

One test reportedly found that they can be moderately toxic to some aquatic species that fish feed on, raising the concern that nanomaterials may accumulate in the food chain. Another showed that largemouth bass exposed to nanoparticles at concentrations of 500 parts per billion, comparable to pollutant levels in port waters, suffered severe damage to brain tissue.

These tests represent what one researcher calls important first steps in toxicity evaluation. They are not regard-ed as conclusive, though, and are not the final word on the safety of nanomaterials. The plastics industry, of course, has plenty of experience in safely handling hazardous, even toxic, materials. Experts say that until tests specific to polymer nanocomposites are conducted, materials producers, compounders, and fabricators should take steps to minimize worker exposure to free particles and ensure that processing conditions contain them during use.

Bibliography

Bruchez, M.P., Jr., and Schultz, P.G., "Organization of 'nanocrystal molecules' using DNA". *Nature*, 1996.

Dahan, M., Laurence, T., Pinaud, F., Chemla, D.S., Alivisatos, A.P., Sauer, M., and Weiss, S., "Time-gated biological imaging by use of colloidal quantum dots". *Opt. Lett.*, 2001.

Empedocles, S.A., Neuhauser, R., and Bawendi, M.G., "Three-dimensional orientation measurements of symmetric single chromophores using polarization microscopy". *Nature*, 1999.

Empedocles, S.A., Neuhauser, R., Shimizu, K., and Bawendi, M.G., "Photoluminescence from Single Semiconductor Nanostructures". *Adv. Mater.*, 1999.

Klein, D.L., Roth, R., Lim, A., Alivisatos, A.P., Colvin, V.L., Schlamp, M.C., and Alivisatos, A.P., "Light Emitting Diodes Made from Cadmium Selenide Nanocrystals and a Semiconducting Polymer". *Nature*, 1994.

Klimov, V.I., Mikhailovsky, A.A., Xu, S., Malko, A., Hollingsworth, J.A., Leatherdale, C.A., Eisler, H., and Bawendi, M.G., "Optical gain and stimulated emission in nanocrystal quantum dots". *Science*, 2000.

Lifshotz, M. and Meilman, M., "Standard Sample for Calibrating Wavelength Scales of Spectral Fluorimeters". *Soviet Journal of Optical Technology*, 1988.

Manna, L., Scher, E.C., Li, L.S., and Alivisatos, A.P., "Epitaxial Growth and Photochemical Annealing of Graded CdS/ZnS Shells on Colloidal CdSe Nanorods". *J Am Chem Soc*, 2002.

Masumoto, Y. and Ogasawara, S., "Photostimulated luminescence of quantum dots". *Journal of Luminescence*, 2000.

Neuhauser, R.G., Shimizu, K.T., Woo, W.K., Empedocles, S.A., and Bawendi, M.G., "Correlation between fluorescence intermittency and spectral diffusion in single semiconductor quantum dots". *Phys Rev Lett*, 2000.

Nirmal, M., Dabbousi, B.O., Bawendi, M.G., Macklin, J.J., Trautman, J.K., Harris, T.D., and Brus, L.E., "Fluorescence intermittency in single cadmium selenide nanocrystals". *Nature*, 1996.

Oda, M., Shen, M.Y., Saito, M., and Goto, T., "Photobrightening of CuBr nanocrystals in PMMA". *Journal of Luminescence*, 2000.

Reisfeld, R., "Inorganic Ions in Glasses and Polycrystalline Pellets as Fluorescence Standard Reference Materials", in *Accuracy in Spectrophotometry and Luminescence Measurements*, R. Mavrodineanu, J.I. Shultz, and O. Menis, Editors. National Bureau of Standards: Gaithersburg, MD. 1973.

Rodríguez-Viejo, J., Heine, H.M.a.J.R., Kuno, M.K., Michel, J., Bawendi, M.G., and Jensen, K.F., "Evidence of photo- and electrodarkening of (CdSe)ZnS quantum dot composites". *Journal of Applied Physics*, 2000.

Schlamp, M.C., Peng, X., and Alivisatos, A.P., "Improved efficiencies in light emitting diodes made with CdSe(CdS) core/shell type nanocrystals and a semiconducting polymer". *Journal of Applied Physics*, 1997.

Tang, Z., Kotov, N.A., and Giersig, M., "Spontaneous Organization of Single CdTe Nanoparticles into Luminescent Nanowires". *Science*, 2002.

Index